Uncle Freddie and the F

ALSO BY ALEX FERGUSON FROM IRON PRESS

The Pineapple King of Jarrow

Uncle Freddie and
The Prince of Wales

Alex Ferguson

First published 2010 by IRON Press
5 Marden Terrace, Cullercoats
Northumberland, NE30 4PD
tel/fax: +44 (0)191 253 1901
ironpress@blueyonder.co.uk
www.ironpress.co.uk

ISBN 978-0-9552450-8-4
Printed by Martins,
Berwick upon Tweed

Typeset in Garamond
Cover design by Brian Grogan
Book design by Kate Jones

IRON Press books are distributed by Central Books
and represented by Inpress Limited,
Collingwood Buildings,
38 Collingwood Street,
Newcastle upon Tyne, NE1 1JF
Tel: +44 (0) 191 229 9555
www.inpressbooks.co.uk

This book is for Charlotte MacAtominey,
hair as red as fire, eyes as green as the sea,
my first love and my last love.

ALEX FERGUSON is a national award winning playwright whose
awards include Writers' Guild Winner Best Radio Comedy/Light
Entertainment, Guinness National Award for Pub Theatre, Plays
International winner, nomination Sony Award for Creative Radio Writing
and Royal Television Society [Regional] nomination for the film *Lads*.
Once upon a time he was the B.B.C.'s Young Poet of the Year. His
Award-Winning radio series *My Uncle Freddie* ran for six seasons on Radio
Four. He is presently working on a new radio series *Days Like This*. He
has worked in theatre, film and television including two seasons with
Corin and Vanessa Redgrave's Moving Theatre Company, at Battersea
Lane and the Riverside, writing the award winning *The Flag* & *Casement*.
Writing for the Northumberland Touring Theatre Company, his work
includes *My Uncle* and *The Stars Look Down*. He was for ten years the
Creative Director of the Bold As Brass Theatre Company. His proudest
achievement is to have been awarded at an early age the Tiny Tots Order
of Merit for keeping the colour within the lines.

Every lad that's born in Jarrow
Has the river in his eyes,
Hears the tides of Tyne turn slowly
In his heart until he dies.

Every lass that's born in Jarrow
Runs the river through her heart
Knowing 'fore she's one and twenty
Love and lover seaward part.

Every bairn that's born in Jarrow,
Urchins of the riverside,
Golden lads and lasses ever,
Swept away upon life's tide.

In The Beginning

IN THE MARKET SQUARE, JARROW, by the sarsaparilla stand there was a man with one arm who played a mouth organ and sang the songs of the Great War. He wasn't a singer of the quality of my Grandfather, but he sang with an aching sadness that filled my young heart with tears I struggled not to show. When he sang 'Keep the Home Fires Burning 'til the Boys come Home Again' my tears would burst the dam.

My Mother, who held me by the hand, would shake me as vigorously as a pepper can and attempt to drag me away. I would resist and beg her to give the singer a penny.

'Yi daft bairn,' she'd say, 'can yi not see he's filling his pockets out of other folks' misery?'

'How can he?' I would argue, 'He only has one arm!'

'His other's inside his body shirt, yi booby, counting the takings!' she'd respond.

Then she'd shake me off and march away to sniff round the market stalls before making her simple purchases. I would stand hypnotised, listening to the one-armed man sing and play his mouth organ.

I have to say soldiers' songs of the Great War were not the most popular in the mid-thirties, but his voice filled my whole being with such an aching longing, evoked such a sense of loss that I weep today to an echo of those songs. We lived daily among men mutilated in mind and body by that great catastrophe. It was the constant backdrop to the theatre of our lives.

When he had finished singing, shaken the spittle from his mouth organ, picked up his cap with its scattering of happence and departed, I would run to find my Mother, seized by a sudden panic that I'd never find her again and be sent to the orphanage. She would seize me by the hand as I ran past oblivious and say, 'Had a good bubble, have yi?'

'No!' I would retort indignantly.

'No? Then I'll give you something to bubble about,' and she'd donate me her bag ton-heavy with cabbage and potatoes that jerked my arms from their sockets.

When I went to the Market with my Grandmother we always stopped to listen and I said to her once, 'Our Mam thinks he's making money out of other folks' misery, Granny.'

'Ya Mam's a bit harsh, pet,' she said, 'Mebbes he's just remembering us of our brave lads that's under Flanders' field. Lads we shouldn't forget.'

She always gave him a penny she could ill-afford.

Shopping done we would proceed to the sarsaparilla stall where a russet-cheeked woman shaped like a cottage loaf would pour the sunlit liquor from jug to jug to provoke a froth that beaded the bright brim with purple bubbles. We much enjoyed this performance and sometimes purchased a gill of aqueous delight that we savoured together, making it last, swelling our cheeks like fleshy balloons, reluctant to release the tasteful treat into our eager throats. It was a moment of supreme happiness.

At that time I had no understanding that my Grandmother was mourning still my Uncle Alex pushing up the poppies on Flanders field. Nor had I any comprehension of the tears of joy my Grandmother shed when I was born one dark December evening. My Mother pressed the newborn into her arms and declared his name Alexander.

Thus did I tumble into this world, in the bedroom of Number One, Hurworth Place, Jarrow on Tyne, missing Christmas by two days, breathing in my Grandmother's bronchial breath, washed by her tremulous tears, to be wrapped in the best towel while Auntie Bella and Mrs.

Dougherty, the babby wife, attended to my Mother. Naught did I know of the damper I had put on the festivities by my reluctance to appear before Christmas. In later years my sisters, Nancy and Peggy, made their disapproval very clear. To the encouragement of the family my Mother had bounced down our stairs, step by step, a dozen times or more, but to no avail. I was not to be shaken or stirred.

Had the Mad Hatter and the March Hare been present on that inauspicious evening, they would surely have cried out, 'No room, no room!' with some justification.

Our accommodation was somewhat limited. We had three rooms and the cupboard on the landing. Granny and Grandad Fergie slept in the kitchen. My sisters slept in the Room and my Mother slept in the bedroom. My Father being a night shift baker at Jarrow Co-operative Society slept during the day. Downstairs in Number Three lived my Auntie Bella and Uncle Freddie.

There were periods when my grandparents were not with us. As a child I was not aware that my Grandfather was an alcoholic and vanished as the seasons to Saint Mark's Retreat. My saintly Grandmother vanished also to care for him.

On the evening of my birth, my Father, on his tin leg, was filling the ovens at the bakery while downstairs my Uncle Freddie and Grandad Fergie were playing Snakes and Ladders with my sisters, Nancy and Peggy who had their collective eye on my grandfather. Grandad Fergie was not to be trusted and would cheat unless closely supervised. Upstairs the women were dealing with the fundamentals of life; blood, pain and joy. My sisters were very disappointed I wasn't a girl. I had also previously disappointed them by not being the baby Jesus.

I had entered a world of grey clouds and rainy skies, wet cobbles and shining slates, handcarts and horses and carts, smoky chimneys and cigarette cards, rackety lorries and steam trains. I heard the morning and evening rattle of the men's boots going to and from their work, the hooters from the yards, the voices of the fishwives peddling their wares, the coal men, the muck men, the tally men, all the noisy flowing traffic of the back lanes. I was to grow accustomed to the uproar, seemingly of an endless war fought over the acres of Palmer's Shipyard, the heart of

Jarrow, the endless racket of the riveting hammers and the clamour of steel. I was to fall asleep, lulled by my Mother's milk, to the lullaby of the steam trains across Albert Road coming up from Shields to Newcastle and down from Newcastle to Shields. I awoke to the soundless sounds of the river, of the turning tides of Tyne flowing through my blood as they will ebb and flow until the last beat of my heart.

It all came to an end in 1933 when Palmer's Shipyard closed its gates forever and proud, hardworking Jarrow died. I had arrived in good time for the Great Depression.

Yet in the difficult years of a Thirties childhood I never felt deprived. I never felt I lacked for anything. I lived among people who loved me. When Palmer's closed and no one needed my Uncle Freddie for a shipwright, he became my constant companion. I loved him with all my heart.

In our wanderings together he told me many wonderful stories and we met the most astonishing people; people you would never expect to meet in Jarrow unless, of course, you were with my Uncle Freddie and me.

One

So it was that one summer's day we found ourselves, my beloved Uncle Freddie and I, in a shabby coble, borrowed from Elijah Lawes, lying off the Shields light, in the shadow of the castle wall of the great stone pier, with a bag full of mackerel at our feet, waiting for the tide to turn, to scull back up-river to the Satellite quay. A bag of mackerel? I tell you now and only once, fresh mackerel is far tastier than any salmon. My Mother cooked mackerel pie to tempt the angels.

We had stopped fishing because as Uncle Freddie said, 'Never take too much, never take too many. Just enough. Then, mebbes, bonny lad, when you come back another time, there'll still be fish to catch.'

He was dozing peacefully in the bow, his face shadowed by the circling of the wakeful herring gulls as I watched a grubby collier making its way down the fairway to pass out through the piers and onto the open sea. As the collier passed the coble we bounced on her swell, rising and falling with arrhythmic grace. I watched with admiration the coaly-faced collier boy moving as a dancer from hatch to hatch, carrying the skipper's mug of tea from the galley without spilling a drop and wished with all my heart that I was that boy, dancing the collier deck, outward bound, to destinations beyond my imagining. Uncle Freddie stirred as the collier slipped by and lifted the coble's bow as we rode her wake.

Can you hear that collier's heart beat? Can you feel the salty sharpness of the smoky breeze on your face? Can you smell the enduring scent of burning coal and hot oil? Can you hear the collier's fading pistons falter as she broaches the bar and lifts to the outward sea? Can you see the collier boy swinging down from the wheelhouse? Do you see him raise a hand in salute to the boy in the coble bouncing in the shadow of the pier wall? How grateful is the boy to be so honoured by that august presence! Do you see him raise a delighted, faltering hand in greeting as the collier vanishes round the pier wall bound for Valparaiso or perhaps London's river? Do you hear the silence fall? A murmur of trippers on the pier? The mewling of the gulls? The slap of salt water against our planking? Is it real, d'y'think? Or is it memory playing tricks?

A herring gull landed on our bow. For a moment the bird stared at Uncle Freddie, bright yellow eye questioning, but when he stirred, blinking from under his cap, the herring gull thought better of pecking his nose and floated away across the water, shrieking disappointment.

'Uncle Freddie?' I said.

'Yes, old sausage?' he answered drowsily.

His eyes slowly closed again.

'Are you awake?' I asked, 'Are you there, Uncle Freddie?'

His eyes opened and he raised his head, his cap as if by some hidden mechanism adjusting itself to his movement. He seemed to be considering my question seriously. Uncle Freddie sat up straight and yawned widely enough to have swallowed the inquisitive gull.

'Am I here?' he asked, and before I could offer the obvious answer, 'Lecky, old sausage, do you know, you've stumbled on the thingumyjig which has puzzled philosophers from the year dot?'

'I have? What thingumyjig?'

'The meaning of life itself. Are we here just to make up the numbers? If I wasn't here would it make any difference other than more porridge to share? Are we really here at all? Is life not simply a dream?'

Uncle Freddie stretched and yawned again. The herring gull hovering above our heads made a hasty retreat shrieking offensively.

'And the answer?'

'Spinno, spello. Latin. I snore, therefore I am asleep.'

I laughed at him and felt the tremble of the coble's laughter beneath me.

'You weren't snoring.'

'Wine-doh, win-dar. Similarly Latin. I speak, therefore I am awake,' announced Uncle Freddie, 'What can I do for you, old sausage?'

I said, 'If you weren't here it would make a deal of difference to me.'

'But if I wasn't here how would you know?' he asked.

I said, defiantly, 'I would know,' and he laughed.

'A more winkit omnibus,' he said and reached to ruffle my hair, 'What were you going to ask me?'

I hesitated and said, 'I was going to ask if you would tell me a story, Uncle Freddie. Please.'

He glanced at the great mill pool of the harbour as if to read the tide's clock although I knew that the tides ran in his blood as the farmer knows when to plough and harrow.

'Well now, what sort of story?'

'Any kind of story. A true story is best,' I hastened to add.

Uncle Freddie smiled and said, 'True stories have a habit of turning out very awkward sometimes, old sausage.'

Once I had a dream and in that dream, above the watery pasture of the harbour, above Knott's Flats, stretching to Collingwood's column where the Trafalgar cannon stand mute and dreadful, I read the words, emblazoned upon the sky, HEART'S ACHE, HEART'S EASE. And in this dream my beloved Uncle Freddie and I were sitting off the Tyne piers, in a shabby coble borrowed from Elijah Lawes, with a bag full of mackerel at our feet, waiting for the tide to turn, to scull back up-river to the Satellite quay. In this dream I asked Uncle Freddie what the words meant and he answered me by saying, 'True stories have a habit of turning out very awkward sometimes, old sausage.'

'That shows how much you don't know, Uncle Freddie,' I replied, secure in my youthful folly.

'How much don't I know?' asked my Uncle, 'Do I need a hand cart or a horse and cart?'

I laughed and said, 'Nothing like that! But I've read heaps of books.'

'Have you now?'

'In the end, justice always triumphs, the hero defeats the villain, and the young sweethearts live happily ever after,' I asserted.

My Uncle Freddie shook his head.

'Not always. Not at sea. The sea runs by a different rule book.'

A shadow of gulls fell across us, darkening the day beneath the limestone of the pier. And the sea said, tapping against the planking, it's true, true, true, sometimes terrible things happen that I can't control, all is quiet, quiet, quiet, lapping, lapping, lapping and then, just like a human being I lose control, I rage, I storm, I cry out in rage and terrible, terrible, terrible things happen. The tide lapped against the timbers, so calmly, calmly, calmly, but the afternoon was irrevocably darker.

'Sometimes somebody dies,' I admitted, 'but they die with a serene smile on their face, and they say, "Bless you, my children." Or "I have only done my duty"' And give a long sigh.'

My Uncle asked, 'Is that how it works?'

I was willing to offer a compromise.

'Sometimes they don't give the long sigh,' I explained, 'Sometimes a trembling of the breath signifies their passing.'

Uncle Freddie searched his pockets until he found his empty pipe and inserted it into his mouth to suck thoughtfully, listening to the water or perhaps his inner self.

'Then I best not tell you the sad story of Charlotte Brewster and her two sweethearts,' he announced regretfully.

We sat in silence for a moment or two to consider this momentous announcement. The hovering gulls waited with bated breath and even the day trippers on the pier stopped chirping.

'Two sweethearts?' I said judiciously, 'That's a bit greedy.'

'Davy and Jamie Robson,' my Uncle affirmed.

Intrigued despite my qualms, I asked, 'Brothers? They were brothers?'

Uncle Freddie sucked on his empty pipe.

'Devoted brothers. Siamese twins until the fair Charlotte put in an appearance.'

It had been the most perfect of afternoons, a golden day from the treasury of golden days. Now clouds threatened to darken the sun.

I inquired, 'Is it a very sad story, Uncle Freddie?'

He regarded me solemnly.

'Sad?' asked my Uncle, 'I have seen one-legged sailormen who never said squeak when their legs were ripped off by ravenous sharks, nor never whistled Dixie when their stumps were dipped into boiling tar, surely bucketing tears down their dirty faces when they heard the story of Charlotte Brewster.'

I promised myself there and then that I would forever keep my distance from ravenous sharks and boiling tar. I would learn to whistle Dixie without delay. Yet if the road menders started boiling up tar my Mother would always send me out into the street to get a good lungful for free. She swore it was good for the bronchials and wherever workmen were boiling tar she would march me over and force my head into the fumes. On occasion I very nearly fell into the cauldron without the opportunity to whistle Dixie.

'Buckets of tears?' I asked fearfully.

Uncle Freddie tapped his pipe on the thwarts.

'Gallons, pecks and bushels, old son,' he affirmed.

D'y'think there's any connection between sailors having legs ripped off and their dirty faces? Did they keep falling over when they stood at the washbasin and just give it up as a bad job? Cleanliness is next to godliness, but not if you keep falling over.

I considered my situation.

I admitted, 'I don't know what to do. I'm in a quandary.'

To reprove me Uncle Freddie tapped me with his pipe.

'It's a coble, old son. A decent little crabbing boat. We'll have no name-calling.'

'I want to hear the story,' I said, 'Only...'

It was one of those idyllic summer days taken for granted when we're young. When we believe summer will never end or winter begin. Sky of amethyst blue. Sea smooth as butter. Only a wisp of white cloud threading the needle eye of Tynemouth Priory. And fresh mackerel sweeter than salmon that my Mother in a clean pinny was awaiting to bake in her oven with the iron door.

'Only,' I hesitantly offered.

My Uncle leapt upon the hesitation.

'Only what? Only a rose I bring you? Only the cheapest ingredients are used? Only the destitute may apply? Or is it standing room only?'

I offered, 'Only Our Mam's worried.'

My Uncle stifled a smile saying, 'Wed to Davy Ferguson I'm not surprised.'

When I laughed Uncle Freddie was surprised.

'That's what Auntie Bella says.'

'What?'

'If I say to her, you should take a breather, Auntie Bella, you look tired, she says, Wed to your Uncle Freddie, are you surprised?'

Shared laughter is the world's greatest music. It was one of those days, the red-hot pepper days of life. We'd slipped down the tide, as Uncle Freddie said, like treacle down a warm spoon and anchored beyond the castle wall of the pier where the green North Sea runs out to the end of the world. When we fished, the mackerel came dancing up the line, fools chasing after feathers, eager to enter the boat, dancing a jig on the boards until the rainbow died. It was the rarest of days, a Cape Triangular stamp of a day.

Uncle Freddie said, 'One day, Lecky, old son, when you're big enough to take the shock.'

He appeared ominously serious, his brow dark, his pipe wagging like a magistrate's wig. He paused in mid-sentence.

I responded indignantly, 'I can take a shock!'

'When you're old enough,' my Uncle continued, 'I'll explain to you about the G.F.C.'

'Gateshead Football Club?'

'The Great Female Conspiracy to Take Over the World.'

The herring gulls circled lower to eavesdrop on this startling revelation. This didn't concern us unless they dropped something else. I drew closer to Uncle Freddie.

'This Conspiracy,' I asked, 'I've never heard of it. When does it start?'

Uncle Freddie answered sadly, 'It's already started, old sausage.'

We sat in silence, listening to the sea.

'To take over the world?' I said.

Uncle Freddie nodded.

'To take over the world,' he repeated.

'I don't believe it,' I asserted, 'Not Our Mam.'

Uncle Freddie sighed.

'*Only* Our Mam's *worried*,' he reminded me.

When we'd caught enough mackerel to feed the Fergies and Mrs. Chamberlain's brood next door, and Grandad twice over, Uncle Freddie had packed up the lines and settled himself to snooze in the bow, spinno, spello, while I watched the smoke shadows pass on the horizon and wondered, wine-doh, win-dar, which way to Valparaiso, which wind for Trincomalee. Such is happiness, as fleeting as the diving cormorant. Now I had a flea in my shirt.

'This G.F.C.?' I asked, 'Is it worse than the Zionist Conspiracy?'

'A mere piccadilly. A fanciful fiction.'

'Worse even than the Bolshevik threat of World Dominoes?'

'Double six every time,' Uncle Freddie lamented.

'What about the Yellow Peril?' I suggested.

Uncle Freddie laughed bitterly and bit down on his empty pipe.

'Dysentery's a park treat compared to the threat hovering over mankind from the GFC.'

I bit on the bullet.

'You're sure Our Mam's in it?'

'Up to her neck,' he assured me.

I clutched at straws and asked, 'Not Auntie Bella?'

The great man was silent for a moment, and then admitted, 'I'm ashamed to say she is worse.'

'How is it I've never noticed?' I complained.

Our little world was suddenly overshadowed as one of Masefield's dirty British coasters came butting in from the North Sea, smoke stack streaming, skipper in a hurry to reach the staithes, lay cables and secure, engine idle, to catch a tram to Walker to a canny wife, a tea that didn't slide about on the table and a bed that didn't throw him on the floor. The coaster gave a hoot of indignation at our presence and left us dancing like the shuggy boats at Whitley Bay fairground.

When the pier had apparently stopped dancing up and down I asked Uncle Freddie again, 'How have I never noticed?'

'Because,' answered my Uncle, 'women are very clever creatures, old son. Some favour a dog or a horse for intelligence, but women are cleverer by far.'

'How'd'y'mean?'

My wise Uncle paused for a moment and then posed the question, 'Have you ever seen ivy growing? I mean, actually on the move?'

I shook my head.

'No.'

Uncle Freddie wagged his pipe in my face.

'But the next minute you look, it has the house in a tight grip, throttling the chimbley.'

I digested this startling news slowly before replying.

'But there's no ivy in Hurworth Place?'

Uncle Freddie sighed and shook his head at me.

'What?' I asked.

'What's your Mam worried about now?'

The herring gulls flocked closer. I took a deep breath and replied, 'Our Mam says, if I let you fill my head with your nonsense, there won't be room for anything else.'

It must've hurt him deeply when I repeated my Mother's words, but he smiled and ruffled my hair. When I was that skinny bairn, my Uncle Freddie had plenty of time to fill my head with nonsense because the world didn't need him and his marrers any more. Those who survived had fought the Kaiser to a standstill and when they came home, they didn't expect a land fit for heroes. They wanted their jobs back at Palmer's to feed their families. But when the bankers shut the yard, Jarrow died. In this misfortune, when others turned to drink and despair, to anger or apathy, Freddie Dean lit the fire of my imagination.

'Oh, aye?' Uncle Freddie asked, 'What sort of item does Mary want you to save space for then?'

I said, 'When I go to the Grammar School,' and hesitated.

'Oh, that's how the wind lies!' he cried, relieved.

I hastened to inform him, 'There'll be French, German, Latin and Mathematics and Science to worry about. Our Mam's worried I won't fit them all in.'

Uncle Freddie laughed and challenged me.

'*When* you go to the Grammar School? You've had an invitation, have you? No need to pass any examination, then?'

'No, but you said, "Never say *if*, always say *when*. Then roll up your sleeves and do it." '

My Uncle laughed, and said, 'So not everything I tell yi's nonsense, eh?'

'I never said it was!' I retorted.

'Tide's on the turn,' said my Uncle.

'I'll get the anchor,' I said and scrambled forrard.

Two

MY MOTHER HELD A VERY SIMPLE VIEW of life. In the saintly-simple sense. Like Nolly Goldsmith, she wondered that such a little head could hold so much. And worried that mine wouldn't. The next great watershed in my life was to be the Scholarship to Jarrow Grammar School. My Mother wanted me to keep some cupboard space.

At sixteen, clutching my Matriculation Certificate, I would obtain a position with the London and North-Eastern Railway Company. I would become the booking clerk at Jarrow station, safe behind three inches of solid oak, passing out cardboard and receiving silver coinage. Behind me in my cosy cabin I would have my very own kettle on my very own stove, my very own teapot and very own cup and saucer and a tin of Little Gem biscuits. I would carry in my head every station, every ticket price, every time of every train on the London and North-Eastern Railway and I would dispense this knowledge on request to every putative passenger. I would be respected, looked up to, admired even and people would say, 'There goes Mister Ferguson! He works for the L.N.E.R. and I do believe he has his very own umbrella!'

This was my Mother's simple dream for me. For her son to be safe and have the prospect of a pension. Not to labour in all weathers, soaking wet one day, and freezing the next. Never to be laid off. Never to suffer the anguish of unemployment. Never to suffer injury, be burnt, cast a finger, lose a limb, or be blinded in the furnace mouth. I was to be in a safe, warm, clean, well-lighted place and use my mind to earn my daily bread.

It was her plan that I was to be the first of our family not to work with the rain, wind and snow on their backs, not to be sent into service like my sisters, not to work the night shift like my Father, a journeyman baker on one leg. Not to be treated like an animal or turned away like a broken horse.

I was to be the booking clerk at Jarrow Station where she could see me every day, even if she didn't approach the window. It would be enough for her to know that I had escaped from the world in which she laboured. She would pull the shawl about her shoulders and go about her business, climbing the steps that carried her over the railway, content to wash, iron and mend other folks' clothes and bedding. This was her dream for her son because she loved me.

Uncle Freddie stood at the stern of the coble and began to scull, to weave a figure of eight pattern with the oar that would drive us steadily up the fairway towards the Groyne tower and its short pier defending the mouth of the Tyne. I sat down and listened to the song of the water sliding along the coble's flanks as we rode our waterhorse with the late afternoon sun turning the harbour bowl to a mirror of gold.

I said, 'Tell me about Charlotte Brewster. Please?'

The sculling oar described its magical figure of eight and the coble, like a tired hound, faithfully continued its homeward track.

'Please?'

Uncle Freddie said, 'Fifty years ago the prettiest girl in Burnmouth was Charlotte Brewster.'

'What did she look like?' I enquired.

'Her hair was red as fire and her eyes as green as the sea.'

'Did you get that out of a song?' I asked suspiciously, 'You said this was a true story!'

'D'y'want to hear the story or not?' asked my uncle, 'The true story of Charlotte Brewster?'

He looked down upon me, his muscular right arm weaving its magic.

The coble floated in the sunlight, moving seemingly without motion towards the river's mouth, as such a launch might have carried the mortally-stricken Arthur to the Vale of Avalon. I nodded up at him.

'Please?'

Uncle Freddie changed hands on the sculling oar without breaking rhythm.

'All the fisher lads were after Charlotte,' he declared, 'but she favoured the Robson brothers, Davy and Jamie. The problem was she couldn't make up her mind two minutes together who it was to be. Would it be Davy? Would it be Jamie?'

The sculling oar echoed the rhythm of the words. *Would it be Davy?* the scull sang to the water. *Would it be Jamie?* the water echoed to the scull.

'Why couldn't she make up her mind?' I asked anxiously, 'Did one have a squint? Bad breath? The school nurse can kill nits just by breathing on them.'

'Davy and Jamie were both fine-looking lads,' my uncle answered, 'Strong as oaks. Like as two peas in a pod. Bobby dazzler fishermen who could smell where the fish was. And that was their undoing, you might say.'

'But why couldn't she make up her mind?' I persisted.

Uncle Freddie explained, 'Charlotte was just a young lass, old son. Lasses are like the tides of Tyne. Forever changing. Besides it's a woman's prepositive to keep the men dangling.'

I considered these wise words and decided if ever I were in such a delicate situation I would keep my feet firmly on the deck. I remembered poor Mr. Chamberlain dangling from the upstairs windowsill while old Mrs. Gallagher belaboured his fingers with her stick because she'd forgotten he was going to clean her window. Before she died Mrs. Gallagher forgot everybody and everything, even the name of her cat. Mr. Chamberlain said the six weeks he spent in Palmer's Hospital was like a holiday, what with the community singing and the grub being champion.

'But worse than that,' my Uncle continued, 'was what it was doing to the lads. It was causing murder and mayhem in Burnmouth, turning devoted brothers into bitter enemies. Sooner or later Davy and Jamie were going to give each other more than the odd smack in the gob. So Charlotte decided. Or mebbes her Father decided for her.

That there should be a contest to win her hand.'

The coble swam silently towards the river's mouth, every nail, every piece of brass and copper, every plank, listening avidly to Uncle Freddie's tale. I gasped in astonishment.

'Like the judgement of Paris! When Paris gave the golden apple to Aphrodite!'

The rhythm of the scull almost paused.

'This was about fish,' stated the storyteller, 'Not parly-vooing Froggies!'

'No, no! Aphrodite helped Paris carry off Helen, the most beautiful woman in the world,' I explained earnestly.

Uncle Freddie changed hands on the scull, but otherwise ignored my helpful intervention.

'So when Charlotte said she would marry whichever of the lads landed the most weight of fish by Christmas Day, they both agreed.'

I was astonished.

'It would've been better if they'd have had to wrestle a Cullercoats fishwife,' I said, feeling somewhat disappointed, 'Annie Sparks threw all three of the pollis into Cullercoats harbour when they came to take her for being drunk. They're going to wait now until they get more men.'

As the pendulum of a clock Uncle Freddie's arm performed its rhythmic magic, but the coble was silent.

'Go on, Uncle Freddie!' I cried.

'Only if you've finished with the latest news from the Police Gazette.'

'Sorry.'

'Davy and Jamie went at it hammer and tongs. Their cobles were scarcely ever off the water. September, October, November. First Davy was ahead. Then Jamie. Davy would be landing on Burnmouth beach as Jamie was pushing off. But never a word passed between them.'

'Why not?' I asked.

'They'd begun to hate one another,' the storyteller recounted.

'You said they were like Siamese twins?'

Uncle Freddie recited sadly, 'When love comes in the window, common sense shoots out the door.'

As I pondered on this truth my Uncle continued with the tragic story of Charlotte and the Brothers Torn Apart by Love.

'Anyway, it was neck and neck into December. Scarcely a stone of fish between them. But the weather was setting into winter.'

The word winter struck me like an icy blast on that heavensweet afternoon.

I cried, 'One of them's not going to get drownded, are they, Uncle Freddie? They're not, are they? Please, don't let anybody die!'

It seemed the sky had darkened, Tynemouth cliffs curtained by rain, a gale was blowing from the Black Middens, a deadly sea was rising, and every matchbox craft was running for shelter, every rotten sail straining at the seams, every fraying cord fretting, every coble losing way, tiring arms pulling on the flailing oars, thwarts awash with angry water, ankle deep within and deathly deep without.

Uncle Freddie said, 'Christmas Eve, it was blowing a gale, but neither lad would give up. If Davy was going out then Jamie would go. Their Mother begged them to stay ashore. But no, the lads were demented and with a terrible tussle they got the cobles through the surf and away.'

My Uncle Freddie was the best storyteller I ever knew. At my Mother's knee I learned to read, write and count. At Dunn Street School, I pretended to learn to read, write and count all over again, and not to make a squeak when the cane rose and fell, but it was an unemployed shipwright who taught me to live in my head. Uncle Freddie built me the vessel in which I've sailed my whole life long, the good ship Imagination.

I was trying not to believe that something terrible was going to happen, but I was no longer in a summerday coble making its way past the Groyne into the calm of the river. I was helpless, stranded on the midnight sands at Burnmouth with the fisher folk, straining eyes desperately seaward for a glimpse of two cobles through the mountainous seas.

Uncle Freddie, eyes straining into the dark sea of that Christmas Eve at Burnmouth, said, 'Bonfires were lit on the beach and the whole village waited out the night, praying for the lads' safe return. Then at last, a shout went up as the dawn shapes of the cobles were seen heading for the beach.'

I cried, 'Thank you, oh, thank you!'

I stood in that dawn with the roaring of the sea and the wilderness of the wind in my ears.

'But so near and yet so far, joy became terror when both cobles overturned and threw the lads into the raging sea,' my Uncle cried.

I shut my eyes and struggled to blot out the terrible scene.

'I don't want to listen any more!' I cried.

Uncle Freddie reported, 'Thankfully two black heads bobbed above the foam!'

'Hoorah!' I cried.

'The brothers began to swim for shore. Every tongue on the beach was frozen except Charlotte's. Then the lass cried out. "Jamie," she cried, "Jamie! Swim to me, my love, swim to me, Jamie!"'

I cried, 'What about Davy?'

'Davy heard the voice too and, heartbroken, turned to swim towards the open sea,' answered Uncle Freddie and his voice trembled.

'Oh, no!'

The storyteller declared, 'Worse was to follow.'

'What could be worse?'

'Jamie swam to save his brother and the sea took them both.'

We stood desolate on that mournful shore. No one moved but Charlotte, who fled weeping from the strand. The sea roared its undiminished hunger and the surf crashed on the sands, demanding its mortal rent.

The coble entered the river. A fisherman sat hunched on the Groyne, the internal optimist. A woman with a child and a toddler pointed us out to her children as we moved past in stately fashion. Were her children looking at me as I had regarded the collier boy, with awe and wonderment, as at a godling? I raised a hand in salute and her children waved enthusiastically. I dried my eyes and said, 'I don't understand that story.'

Uncle Freddie said, 'You see, when it came to it, he loved his brother more than the lass.'

'But he dies!' I objected, 'They both died!'

'Dying's not the worst thing that can happen, old sausage,' my Uncle declaimed, 'Somehow it matters how you die.'

I sat and considered this assertion as my Uncle stroked the coble steadily up river.

'I think,' I said, 'That's the most wonderful story you've ever told me, Uncle Freddie,' and, on impulse, 'What happened to Charlotte? Did she die of a broken heart, and with her last, long, lingering breath whisper the name of her lost sweetheart?'

Uncle Freddie laughed and answered, 'Six months later she married a travelling butcher from Kelso called Jimmy MacAtominey. Her Mam and Dad were set up for life with stewing steak and sausage.'

I sat stunned as a codfish hitting the bottom boards.

'MacAtominey's butcher's shop down Albert Road?'

My Uncle nodded, saying, 'The very same. Jimmy's son runs it now. Jimmy's the Grandad.'

'And Charlotte married him?'

'He wasn't a Grandad then.'

I listened to the rhythm of the scull and the mewling of the gulls in a salty silence. Life has such twists and turns. As when you're on your way to the Kino on a Saturday with a thrupenny bit in your pocket and a dream of Shirley Temple in your head. Then you find there's a hole in your pocket and the silver has fled as the dreams of the silver screen.

'But they did live happily ever after?'

Uncle Freddie said, 'They lived in MacAtominey's caravan.'

'Then they did,' I declared, 'It says so in the poem. "I wish I was a gypsy man and lived my life in a caravan."'

'Not with a dozen dead pigs for company you wouldn't.'

'But they were happy?' I urged.

Changing hands on the scull, Uncle Freddie replied, 'Charlotte had thirteen bairns. I doubt she had time to ask herself if she was happy or not.'

I marvelled at the image of these wild and beautiful girls.

'With hair as red as fire and eyes as green as the sea?' I questioned.

Uncle Freddie shook his head.

'Sadly, no. Every last one of her bairns took after MacAtominey who would've had his throat cut many a time if he hadn't been the one in the pigpen wearing check trousers.'

Defiantly I offered, 'Well, I still think that counts as living happily.'

'Which is more than the pigs did,' my Uncle countered, 'Charlotte's black puddens were famous from Billingham to Berwick.'

We sculled steadily upriver towards the Satellite quay in silence as I pondered on life's vagaries.

Three

'HALLO!' SAID UNCLE FREDDIE, 'What's up with him?'

A dinghy was drifting down on us, carried seaward by the current. A young man was standing up in the dinghy grasping an oar. The young man, a stranger, called out to us, 'Ahoy, there! I say, boatman, ahoy there!'

Uncle Freddie and I exchanged surprised glances.

'Who's he shouting at?' asked my Uncle.

'There's only us,' I replied.

Uncle Freddie held the coble against the current.

'He's not a local lad, then?' he said, 'What sort of language is that? *Ahoy there, boatman!*'

The young man, struggling to stay upright, the dinghy turning broadside, called to us again, 'I say, boatman, can you hear me? Ahoy there!'

Travelling with the dinghy, but loose in the water, was an oar.

'He's lost an oar, Uncle Freddie,' I cried.

'Then he's on his way to Denmark,' my Uncle decided, 'We'd best sort him out.'

He bent to the scull to bring us alongside the errant dinghy.

'I say, boatman! I wonder if you might render me assistance?' cried the young man, oblivious to Uncle Freddie's manoeuvring of the coble.

'Coming, sir!' my Uncle called, and mildly exasperated, 'Just keep your trousers on, sir!'

As Uncle Freddie struggled to align the coble with the dinghy that was enjoying its taste of freedom, I had time to note the young man's style of dress.

'He's got very funny trousers,' I noted, 'They only come halfway down his legs.'

Wrestling with the scull, Uncle Freddie remarked, 'Plus fours. A sure sign of good breeding.'

'I never knew that! Could he be a toff? We've never rescued a toff before!'

'People who wear plus-fours are entitled to shout, "render me assistance",' my Uncle assured me, 'We may even see sight of a shilling or even a half-a-crown.'

Uncle Freddie manoeuvred the coble skilfully to come alongside the drifting dinghy. At that moment the young man lost the second oar and reaching to catch it, fell down in the dinghy, which responded by sheering away from us, out of reach of the boat hook I was wielding. The young man struggled to his feet, rendering his situation even more perilous.

'I'm sorry,' he cried, wobbling woefully, 'I do apologise! I'm afraid I'm not frightfully good at this messing about in boats business!'

As he struggled to retrieve the situation, my Uncle Freddie called reassuringly 'No apologies necessary, sir! We'll have you aboard in two shakes! If you'd be so good as to sit down, sir?' and under his breath to me, 'We'll be sending your Mam a postcard from Copenhagen at this rate.'

The young man sat down and called, 'I'm being a frightful nuisance, I know. So good of you to take the trouble!'

'No trouble at all, sir,' called my Uncle, struggling with a rising tide, and to me, 'The problem is he's topping eight knots and we're pushing four.'

That the lighter dinghy was drifting faster than the coble blinded us to the oncoming danger that an outgoing collier was bearing down on us. It was only when the exasperated skipper blew his steam whistle and his engines thundered in our ears that we realised we had company.

The collier ran down the dinghy as a man might step on a matchbox and steamed on blithely towards the piers' mouth and the open sea.

As the sooty smog from his smoke stack dissipated we gazed upon an empty river.

'That collier ran him down,' I stated most obviously.

'Like a tom cat under a steam roller,' Uncle Freddie agreed.

'There!' I cried and as Uncle Freddie sculled across current I scooped up the young man's cap with the boat hook. It was a sporty cap that had sat on his head like a large dinner plate. Sadly his head was now parted from its embellishment.

'Can't you see him anywhere?' I asked.

Uncle Freddie shook his head.

'I think you should prepare yourself for the worst, old sausage. Our Lord Fauntleroy might be a gonner,' he suggested.

I was wondering whether it was distasteful to mention the loss of a shilling or even half-a-crown when something rapped on the coble's flank and a now familiar voice said, 'I say, boatman, I'm sorry to bother you, but might I come aboard?'

'He's here!' I cried.

And he was indeed here, our young gentleman! Clinging to the coble's planking, auburn hair plastered to his scalp and Fair Isle jumper like seaweed below the wavering waterline.

'Oh, Uncle Freddie, it's just like Charlotte Brewster and Davy and Jamie, but even better!' I cried.

Uncle Freddie tied off the scull as a sea anchor and came to assist our survivor.

'Stand by with the boat hook,' he ordered me, and to the young man, 'Don't panic, sir! We'll soon have you aboard.'

'Don't know what happened to the dinghy,' said the young man, between mouthfuls of salty water, 'One moment the beastly thing was there and then! Whoosh, I'm in the drink! Reminds one of a bit of a tiffle at Henley. Do you go to Henley?'

'Not recently,' said Uncle Freddie, slipping a rope around the young man, 'Now what I want you to do is use the water to push yourself up, and we'll haul you inboard!'

'Very decent of you to give a chap a hand!' the young man said, 'And we haven't even been introduced, have we?'

Uncle Freddie said, 'Never mind about that now, sir. Just use the water as a springboard and push yourself up. I'll haul you inboard.'

'Right-ho! Push myself up? Right-ho!'

'Here we go,' said my uncle, 'On the mark of three! Big breath! One. Two. Three!'

The young man in plus fours vanished into the green depths. Uncle Freddie and I gazed at each other in wonder.

'What the?' cried my Uncle.

'Where's he gone now?' I cried.

A floundering, drowning, gasping figure surfaced under our noses.

'Sorry! Frightfully sorry!' he gasped and vanished again.

'Boat hook!' Uncle Freddie called. I put it in his hand.

When our hapless young man rose spluttering to the surface again Uncle Freddie expertly caught him with the boat hook to which the young man clung, struggling for breath.

'Terribly sorry, old boy,' cried our salvage, 'Went wrong somehow. Too many ciggies I shouldn't wonder.'

Uncle Freddie wordlessly heaved him over the thwarts into the coble where he lay on the bottom boards, gasping for breath, resting his head on a pillow of mackerel within our fish bag.

'Terribly sorry to be such a nuisance,' he cried and abruptly dragged himself up to vomit over the side into the green water that mirrored the hue of his face.

'No bother,' my Uncle said, 'Mind, you've lost a good dinner there, sir. But if you get the water up, all the better. It'll save the typhoid later.'

'Thank you. Awfully decent of you to save my life,' replied our new friend gratefully.

'No bother, sir, no bother at all. Glad to be of service. You go and sit up in the bow, sir. You'll get the fresh air in your face,' advised my Uncle compassionately.

The young man went to sit in the bow and took out a tortoiseshell cigarette holder and silver cigarette case. He lit a cigarette and began coughing. I inhaled deeply the exotic perfume of Turkish tobacco.

'That's right, sir,' Uncle Freddie counselled, 'You have yourself a cigarette. Puff away, sir. It'll clear your lungs. They tell me it's just the job after vigorous exercise or exertion. For them as can afford it.'

Uncle Freddie stuck his empty pipe in his mouth, but the hint was ignored.

As he sculled us upriver towards the Satellite quay, my Uncle said, quietly to me, 'Well, Lecky, I don't know about you, but I doubt anybody's landed a stranger fish today.'

'Wha'd'y'mean?'

'You have noticed his face is very familiar?'

I shook my head.

'Who is it, Uncle Freddie?'

'Don't you recognise him?' he whispered to me.

I studied the stranger's face as he sat, in profile, cigarette holder in hand, oversize dinner plate cap on head, plus fours and Argyle stockings: the very portrait of damp elegance.

'It's not Wally Simpson who runs the chip shop in Connaught Terrace, is it? He's got a cigarette holder. It impresses customers no end to have him wrap up their carry-oot with a cigarette holder in one hand and the vinegar bottle in the other.'

'Close,' said Uncle Freddie, 'It's Edward.'

I was stumped for an answer.

'I don't know any Edwards. Unless he's a potato.'

My Uncle changed arms on the scull and bent closer to me.

He whispered, 'The Prince of Wales, old sausage!'

'The Prince of Wales,' I replied, disbelievingly.

Uncle Freddie nodded emphatically.

'Your future king. When his present Majesty, God bless him, hands in his irons, that is. Which is any minute now.'

'The Prince of Wales!' I cried with mounting excitement.

'Dragged out of the Tyne like a sack of drowned moggies. Would you believe it?' replied my dear Uncle.

Would you believe it? It may sound incredible, but it was no surprise to Uncle Freddie and me. So many ley lines converge at Jarrow that famous people were irresistibly drawn to the waters of Tyne. Or maybe it was the delicious, crispy battered cod at Simpson's chip shop?

Four

THERE ARE TIMES WHEN, DOZING in my chair as an old man does, I almost find myself home again in Auntie Bella's kitchen. The ticking of a clock? The contented humming of a kettle on a hob? The shift of coal in an open fire? The rattle of fire irons? The very particular clunk of her iron oven door? The sweet aroma of freshly ironed linen? Some simple sound or scent provokes the memory and I awake to an overwhelming sense of loss.

Auntie Bella's kitchen was a sanctuary, a pool of calm, a refuge against the storm where we would squat together on her fender, work done, and take turns to read a sixpenny romance one to another. Or I would read to Auntie Bella while she ironed other folks' linen, the flat irons being returned to the fire over my head by way of punctuation.

But today was a very different occasion. We were comfortably ensconced in the familiar warmth of Auntie Bella's kitchen, downstairs in Number Three, Hurworth Place, just the Heir To The Throne, reclining in Auntie Bella's chair, Uncle Freddie and me, sipping tea.

'This is the first time ever,' I whispered to Uncle Freddie, 'that we've ever had plus fours hanging up to dry in Hurworth Place.'

'A right royal occasion indeed,' he agreed.

A sudden inspiration struck me.

'Can Norman Richardson come in to see his underpants?' I suggested quietly, 'He wouldn't be any bother.'

My Uncle Freddie shook his head gravely.

'Sorry, old son. We must respect the Prince's anonymity.'

I whispered, 'Our Mam just says, make sure you wash your private parts.'

'We could squeeze another cup out of the pot if you're ready, sir,' my Uncle suggested to the Heir To The Throne.

'Is it China tea, Freddie?' asked the Prince.

'The pot is, sir,' my Uncle responded, 'Bella would never touch bakelite.'

The Prince indicated his approval and Uncle Freddie refilled his cup.

'You alright there, sir?'

'Very comfortable indeed. And I'm jolly grateful to you, Freddie, old man, for saving my life. And offering the hospitality of your own home. I shall be forever in your debt.'

I wondered if this was the time to mention a shilling or even half-a-crown, but decided against it. Nothing had fallen out of his plus fours when Uncle Freddie hung them up in front of the fire, which surprised me. I would've thought he was old enough to have a front door key to the Palace.

Our front door key hung on a string behind the letterbox. If you wanted in, you reached through the letterbox and pulled the key out to open the door. That wouldn't do for a Palace, what with Anarchists, Bolsheviks and foreign ambassadors, but it worked fine for us. If Grandad Fergie was extremely intoxicated, which happened to him sometimes, through no fault of his own, whoever brought him home would simply open the front door and lie him down in the bottom passage, as he wouldn't be allowed upstairs anyway. Once, they deposited two old men in our bottom passage ,which my Mother thought a bit much, as neither one was Grandad Fergie.

The Prince asked, 'Do you play golf, Freddie?'

'No, sir,' admitted my Uncle, shaking his head sadly as if playing golf was his heart's desire, but circumstances forbade.

'What do you do for sport?'

'I pick coals on the pit heap, sir.'

The Prince considered this reply.

'Is there a handicap?' he asked.

'If you're old and the sack's heavy, I suppose there is,' Uncle Freddie replied, 'And when the pollis turns up, there's all the excitement of the chase.'

The Prince laughed.

'I say, it all sounds rather jolly!' he cried, 'Like the old Wall Game, eh? Floreat Etona! Perhaps you might take me to see a game?'

Uncle Freddie looked momentarily bewildered.

'A game?' and then recovered himself, 'Aye, certainly, sir! Any time.'

Uncle Freddie and I exchanged glances of disbelief.

'Splendid!' cried the Heir To The Throne, 'I shall look forward to the occasion.'

The Prince was reclining in Auntie Bella's chair by the blackleaded range, tortoiseshell cigarette holder in hand, a scent of expensive Turkish tobacco in the air, clad in nifty monogrammed vest and underpants of crepe de chine, with me gazing humbly up from the fender while Uncle Freddie did the honours with the Coronation teapot. The Prince looked around at Auntie Bella's neat and tidy kitchen.

'And this is your home, is it, Freddie?'

'This is our humble abode, sir. The wife Bella and me. Just the two damp rooms and the scullery,' my hero replied.

'Isn't there a bathroom?'

'For state occasions,' replied my Uncle, 'We have the zinc bath by the fire. Very cosy. There's a tap by the washhouse for the Spartans and the water closet's down the yard. The earth closet's gone so we're bang up to date.'

Uncle Freddie misunderstood the uncomprehending look on the Prince's face and hurried to offer, 'If you're planning on using the water closet, sir, Lecky'll give the seat a polish and find you some paper without printing on it.'

'You have a lackey?' the Prince questioned.

Uncle Freddie laid a hand on my shoulder.

'No, sir. This is Lecky. My nephew. My wife's sister's son. Only called

Alexander on a Sunday.'

The Prince looked at me as if he had only now seen me for the first time.

I explained, 'We live upstairs. Our Mam and Dad and me. I had two sisters, but they've evaporated.'

The Prince, in puzzlement, asked, 'Evaporated?'

'Gone into service,' said my Uncle.

'At the big hoose at Jedburgh-over-the-Border in rarified Roxburghshire,' I explained.

The Prince's brow cleared.

'Oh, Galloway? First-rate shooting and fishing! D'y'know we knocked down some twelve hundred brace at Oliver's place! In one afternoon! Absolutely top hole!'

'We had two pheasants by post once,' I contributed. 'There was a hundred and seventeen bits of lead in them. We were picking it out of our teeth for days, weren't we, Uncle Freddie?'

'When your sisters come home for Christmas,' smiled the Prince, 'I bet you all have a jolly time, eh?'

'They don't come home at Christmas.'

The Prince was surprised.

'Why ever not?'

'Her Ladyship's family comes home for Christmas so Nancy and Peggy can't. They're very busy. That's what Our Mam says is hardest to bear. Not to see them at Christmas.'

'Oh, I say!' the Prince cried, 'What rotten luck!'

My sisters had been stolen, taken into a faraway place. Too busy slaving at cleaning and washing and scrubbing and curtseying and fetching and carrying ever to be carefree girls again. Never to be my Mother's daughters at Christmas again.

'And what do you do, Freddie?' asked the Prince.

Uncle Freddie said, 'I used to be at Palmer's, sir.'

The Prince brightened, recognising a familiar name.

'Palmer's Water Biscuits, eh? First rate! I always have them at my bedside. D'y'know I've always wanted to know how you got the little holes in the biscuits? Is it done by hand or is there a machine? Whichever it is, it's jolly clever not to break the biscuits.'

My Uncle said, 'No, sir, not Palmer's Biscuits. Palmer's Shipyard.'

The Prince was disappointed.

'I see,' he said, but didn't see.

'We built ships,' offered my Uncle, helpfully, 'But the yard is closed now.'

'And what are you now?'

Uncle Freddie said, 'Surplus to requirement, sir. Like the rest of Jarrow. Palmer's is shut and every man jack's out of work.'

The Prince looked very serious.

'You will forgive me asking, Freddie,' said the Prince, 'But why don't you seek employment elsewhere?'

I admired my Uncle's restraint as he sought to enlighten the Prince as to the situation on Tyneside.

'There is no other employment, sir,' said Uncle Freddie patiently, 'Palmer's has gone. Everybody in Jarrow in one way or another depended on Palmer's. Imagine a row of dominoes, sir. Push the first domino over and all the others fall. That's how it is in Jarrow. And on Tyneside.'

The Heir To The Throne pondered on Uncle Freddie's words, but before he could speak my Uncle said, 'Forgive me asking, sir, but what are you going to do about it?'

The Prince seemed surprised.

'Do about it, Freddie? About what?'

Uncle Freddie and I exchanged glances.

'Ill fares the land,' Uncle Freddie declaimed, 'to hast'ning ills a prey, Where wealth accumulates, and men decay.'

I took up the refrain.

"A bold peasantry, their country's pride, When once destroy'd, can never be supplied."

From the expression on the Prince's face it was obvious that his expensive education hadn't extended to the acquaintance of Oliver Goldsmith.

My Uncle Freddie explained, 'We're what's left of that bold peasantry, sir. In the process of being fragmentised. To England's shame. Do you remember fourteen-eighteen, sir? The terrible sacrifices of life and limb!'

The Prince's face lit up in recognition.

'I certainly do!'

'Then you understand, sir?'

'I jolly well do! Papa insisted I give up being a middie on the HINDUSTAN which was jolly good fun – I've always looked very dashing in whites – to wander around France in ghastly khaki, with Sir John French, looking stern and pointing at things with his stick. The din never ceased. Night and day. Bang, bang, bang!'

My Uncle looked at me in despair.

'Bang, bang, bang,' Uncle Freddie said, 'I remember it well.'

Uncle Freddie wriggled into the forward observation post to relieve his best mate, Jimmy MacAlaney, just as the stick grenade arrived, thrown in hope rather than calculation. Just to let Tommy know the f.o.p. was marked. Jimmy fell on the grenade. Jimmy died and Freddie lived. Bang, bang, bang.

The Prince said, 'Mamma, of course, insisted I shouldn't be allowed anywhere I might be in the least danger.'

'If only other Mothers had insisted on the same, sir,' said my Uncle, regretfully, 'But you did say, "*Something must be done!*"'

'Did I?'

I said, 'In the newsreel at the Kino.'

Uncle Freddie prompted the Heir To The Throne.

'You were visiting a Welsh pit village at the time.'

The Prince offered, apologetically, 'One has to say something.'

Uncle Freddie persisted, saying, 'Your face expressed anger and compassion.'

The Prince's face displayed understanding.

'Oh, that! I was wearing a brand new pair of brogues and I stepped into an absolutely enormous dog poo. Very annoying! I did rather feel something should've been done.'

We sat in silence. The ticking of the clock grew louder. A fall of coals prompted a disappointed Uncle Freddie to ask, 'So you're not here to find out how bad things are on Tyneside?'

The Prince said, 'Actually, I was on the SHAMROCK, What'shisname's yacht. The grocer chappy? Lipstick?'

It took a moment or so before light dawned. Cyril Liddell, the manager of the Humbert Street Co-op, was the only grocer we knew who might have a fancy for lipstick, but if he ever owned a yacht it would now be on the bottom of the West Park Pond.

'Lipton,' said Uncle Freddie, 'Sir Thomas Lipton.'

The Prince slapped his knee in confirmation.

'That's the chap!' he cried, 'We'd put in at Newcastle, and I thought, I'll take the dinghy and punt about and work up a bit of an appetite. Some of these seven course dinners take a bit of swallowing, I can tell you.'

My Uncle Freddie persisted, 'But if you spoke up, sir, people would have to listen! You're the Prince of Wales. Very soon you'll be King! Emperor of India! Defender of the Faith! Then defend us, sir! Not only Jarrow. The whole country's crying out. You could do so much, sir. Think about it, I beg you, give it serious thought.'

The Heir To The Throne sighed deeply and replied, 'I have thought about it, Freddie, jolly hard, and I've come to a decision.'

We awaited his decision with bated breath.

'Yes, sir?'

The Prince shook his head sadly, generously shaking cigarette ash onto Auntie Bella's clippy mat.

'I'm not cut out for this king thing,' he admitted.

Uncle Freddie kept his patience.

'I didn't choose to hammer rivets in the rain, sir,' he suggested, gently, 'But it paid for bread and the rent. We do what we have to do.'

The Prince looked as mournful as a scolded puppy.

'I don't ever want to be king.'

'Uneasy lies the head that wears a crown,' I agreed.

'Quite,' said the Prince.

'You should take it off at night,' I suggested.

My Uncle ignored my helpful suggestion and pressed further.

'But it's your duty, sir. It's what you're born and bred for.'

The Prince sighed an enormous sigh and his undergarments of crepe de chine fluttered in sympathy. He seemed about to weep.

He said, tremulously, 'Not if I cannot have the woman I love.'

Uncle Freddie laughed.

'You, sir? The debonair bachelor prince whose witty ripostes have charmed every princess out of her ivory tower? The playboy of the Wisden world who could have his pick of the world's women from Wurtemburg to Worra-Worra?'

Uncle Freddie fell silent as he glimpsed the tragedy in the young Prince's face.

'The woman I love is as common as you are, Freddie,' the Prince admitted.

My Uncle gasped.

'As low as that, sir?'

The Prince leaned forward in conspiracy and we leaned towards him as willows in the wind.

His voice throbbing with emotion, the Prince said, 'You saved my life today, Freddie Dean. To such a man as you I entrust the secret of my heart.'

'If you feel you must, sir,' Uncle Freddie replied, reluctantly.

Once more our breaths were bated as the Prince braced himself to exclaim, 'I love Mrs. Wallis Simpson.'

I fell off the fender and Uncle Freddie juggled with Auntie Bella's Coronation teapot before he sat down bang and flattened the Coronation tea caddy in his agitation. There reigned a silence too deep for words.

'Mrs. Wallace Simpson?' I ventured.

The Prince nodded and leaned forward to ruffle my hair.

'Yes, my boy, Mrs. Wallis Simpson!'

My Uncle suggested, diplomatically, 'She's not one of your upper crust?'

The Prince smiled.

'She has a nobility beyond rank.'

With the practicality of youth, I asked, 'Does her husband know?'

With the laughter of bravado, the Prince cried, 'That is not my concern! I don't care who knows. I love Mrs. Simpson.'

I thought it only fair to warn him.

'You'd better watch out. If her husband takes the needle.'

My concern was brushed aside as the Prince offered his hand to Uncle Freddie. They shook hands warmly.

'There, Freddie! I have declared my heart and you, dear friend, are the first to know,' the Prince cried gaily.

'My lips are sealed, sir,' my Uncle affirmed.

'I have wrestled with my conscience,' the Prince declared, 'through endless sleepless nights.'

I tried again to join this grave discussion on the future happiness of the nation and the possibility of the Prince being violently parted from his front teeth.

'Well, I'd better warn you Wally Simpson used to be a wrestler. He's a tattoo artiste now. But he probably still remembers how to do it.'

But no one was listening. I could understand now the frustration of Cassandra when the Trojans dragged the fateful Horse into the city.

Uncle Freddie asked, 'But what about Princess Marie Theresa of Hapsburg-Gotha to whose side you rushed at top speed when she fell from her pony at Windsor?'

'She had landed on the lunch hamper,' the Prince explained, 'I was concerned for the pate de fois gras.'

'Pate de fois flat, I would think,' I offered, which I thought rather witty.

'What about our own dear Lady Dorothy, eldest daughter of the Duke of Acklington, who staggered under the stag you shot, from Prickley Fell to Acklington Castle, despite her recent hernia operation?' suggested my Uncle, displaying an unexpected knowledge of the doings of the nobility, gained doubtless from hours spent in the Public Library perusing *Horse & Hounds* and *Country Life*.

'You can't have a Queen Dorothy,' I asserted.

'Quite!' agreed His Royal Highness.

I knew it was all nonsense. There'd been no pottering about on the yacht, no casual punting at Newcastle Quay. Prince Edward's journey down the Tyne had been a lovers' tryst that had gone sadly awry. The Prince of Wales loved Mrs. Wallace Simpson who ran the chip shop in Connaught Terrace with her husband Wally who had the tattoo parlour upstairs in their front room.

The Prince sighed deeply and declared, 'I know they'll all be against me. The Prime Minister. The Archbishop. My Mother. The newspapers. But true love will prevail!'

'That's what Archduke Michael says in THE THRONE OVER-TURNED,' I agreed, 'Just before he gives in and abandons the simple country maiden, Esmeralda.'

'Never!' the Prince cried, 'I shall need all the strength I can summon. But I will never, ever permit us to be separated!'

How did I know it was Mrs. Wallace Simpson? Mrs. Simpson once tried to give my Mother the wrong change for three haddock and chips. My Mother declared, 'I wouldn't trust that woman with the King of England.' That was good enough for me.

'She is too good for me. She is all I have ever dreamt of. A goddess among women,' his Royal Highness proclaimed, 'And most wonderful of all, Freddie, she loves me. She truly loves me. That's the most surprising thing of all, that such a wonderful woman should love me!'

Five

I HEARD THE LATCH OF THE SCULLERY door and the familiar voices and I
was on my feet to greet them when the kitchen door opened and my
Mother and Auntie Bella entered.

'Our Mam! Auntie Bella! Guess who,' but I got no further before I was
interrupted by my maternal parent who was bending upon us a frosty
glance.

'What's going on here?' she cried, her voice hackled with horror.

'Freddie!' my Auntie Bella chimed, similarly arctic in expression, 'What
debauchery have you been up to?'

My Uncle Freddie stumbled to his feet.

'Nothing, my pet, allow me to introduce,' he faltered, but was as
cruelly cut short as Stanley Sidebotham's fingers in his Mother's mangle.
This minor tragedy was an unforeseen asset to Stan in later life as his
fingers could never reach the coins in his trouser pocket bottom.

My Auntie Bella cried, 'Allow you nothing! I want this creature out of
my kitchen now!'

'But Bella, my sweetling,' expostulated my bewildered Uncle, 'This is
Prince Edward. The Prince of Wales!'

Emboldened, I added my two pennorth.

'Your future king, Auntie Bella. When his present Majesty, God bless him, hands in his irons, that is. Which is any minute now.'

Auntie Bella snorted her disbelief.

'And I'm the Queen of the Fairies. I'm ashamed of you, Freddie.'

This formidable lady then turned her fury onto the Heir To The Throne.

'Out! I want you out!'

'Madam, I do assure you,' the Prince assured Auntie Bella, rising from the chair, only to be brusquely interrupted by my Mother.

'No trousers! And he wants to assure you, Bella! Shameless in front of the bairn! Lecky, I hope you've had your eyes closed!'

'He's had his anonymity covered all the time, Our Mam,' I assured her indignantly.

For answer Auntie Bella flung open the kitchen door and pointed dramatically at the back door.

'Out! Out the pair of you! And take the daft clown suit with you!'

For good measure Auntie Bella flung the damp plus fours at the Prince of Wales. It was all splendid Victorian melodrama. Momentarily Auntie Bella seemed lost for words.

'And don't darken my doorstep again?' I suggested, and, 'Ow!' as my Mother twisted my ear, pulling me aside.

'Out!' cried Auntie Bella, 'And don't bring this depraved creature back here again!'

My Uncle Freddie protested, 'But Bella, my precious!'

But it seemed no male member of the family was ever to be allowed to finish a sentence again as Auntie Bella interrupted with a crushing, 'Precious me nothing! Out! Out you go!'

'I do assure you, madam,' the Prince of Wales offered, 'that despite appearances to the contrary–'

Auntie Bella turned her fury onto the hapless Heir To The Throne, clutching his crumpled plus fours.

'Don't you dare assure me! Are you deaf as well as daft? Out! Out of my kitchen toot sweet!'

My Uncle surrendered, moving to the door.

'All right, my angel, we're going. I'll explain everything later.'

The Prince of Wales followed after his discomfited host.

'Thank you very much, madam. It's been a delightful experience.'

'And we can do without your sarcasm!' cried my irate Auntie.

I attempted to follow the Prince, saying, 'You'll be sorry when you find out the truth!'

Which my Mother countered, saying, 'One step outside that door and you'll be sorry. Get yourself back in here!'

'Oh, Our Mam!' I protested, 'Lettis go!'

'Don't say I didn't warn you,' said she in a tone of menace I knew well. The kitchen door closed behind my Uncle and the Prince of Wales.

'You're the ones that'll be sorry,' I retorted defiantly.

'Oh, will we, indeed?' replied my Mother.

'When you wake up in the Tower of London you will be. Do you know who that was?'

'No. And I don't care tuppence.'

I savoured the words.

'That was the Prince of Wales,' I announced.

The two women laughed long and loud.

'Oh, Lecky,' my Auntie cried, 'You are the absolute limit!'

My Mother said, 'D'you expect us to believe that? The Prince of Wales?'

'It's true!' I cried indignantly.

'In Hurworth Place?'

'We fished him out of the river.'

'And we're supposed to believe that? You've got another think coming, my son.'

I responded with. 'You'll have plenty of time to think locked up in the Bloody Tower.'

'Lecky!' cried Auntie Bella, scandalised.

'I think we need soap and water here,' my Mother declared, 'Somebody needs their mouth washed out!'

'It's not swearing,' I explained, 'It's history. It's called that because the walls are soaked in the blood of countless martyrs.'

'I'll give you countless martyrs,' my Mother threatened which was a sure sign she was losing the argument.

'Walls soaked in the blood of,' I countered, 'But it's not swearing.'

'I'll give you walls soaked in the blood of,' she threatened.

She was always threatening me with gifts of stands-to-sense, Alsace-Lorraine, Jarrow Tramways, long division, the Rights of Man, Dolly's Mixture, the White Cliffs of Dover, even MacAtominey's Family Sausage.

Auntie Bella who had been silent during this duel between Mother and son, said, 'The Prince of Wales? Sitting in my kitchen? With no trousers on?'

She seemed torn between seeing it as an outrage or an honour.

I sprang to the defence of the Heir To The Throne.

'He had underpants. I've only ever seen underpants in the catalogue before.'

'And that's another thing that's got to stop,' my maternal parent insisted, 'You sending for catalogues.'

But I was busily proselytising my Auntie.

'Plus fours. And underpants. He must be the Prince of Wales. Stands to sense he must be, Auntie Bella!'

'I'll give you stands to sense in a minute, my lad,' warned the dispenser of bizarre threats.

Auntie Bella shook her head, dissipating the dream of a princely presence in her kitchen.

'Sometimes I worry about you, Lecky,' she decided.

'Well, you'd better start worrying about Mrs. Wallace Simpson instead,' I countered.

My Mother pounced.

'I've told you. Don't mention that woman's name in this house!'

'Why not, Our Mam?'

'Three haddock and chips is one and thruppence, not one and six, that's why,' she declared triumphantly.

Auntie Bella settled the kettle onto the fire and cleared the teapot into her waste bucket.

At the cupboard, looking for the tea caddy, she asked, 'Why should we start worrying about Mrs. Simpson?'

'You'll see. Just you wait and see,' I said with all the confidence of idiot youth.

Auntie Bella, unable to find the tea caddy in its accustomed place, spotted the flattened Rington's caddy on the chair vacated by my dear departed Uncle.

'Whatever has Freddie done to the tea caddy?' she enquired.

'That's when he found out about Mrs. Wallace Simpson and the Prince of Wales,' I explained, 'He was taken by surprise.'

'Upstairs!' my Mother ordered, 'Upstairs now! Before I forget meself!'

Six

Upstairs in Number One, Hurworth Place, we Fergies had the luxury of three rooms, never mind the big cupboard on the landing. The first door on the left was the kitchen where Granny Fergie or my Mother cooked and Granny Fergie baked bread. My grandparents slept in a contraption that folded up during the day into a large sideboard with double doors. The second door to the left was the Room. We always called it The Room. It was where the sewing machine lived and the Good Chair. Now that my sisters were in service I slept in the bed in the corner where the hum of the gas lamp and the presence of my Mother working her needle magic on somebody's shabby pillowslip would soothe me to sleep. The third door on the landing was the bedroom where my Mother kept her lonely vigil by night and my Father slept by day. By Hurworth Place standards, we were middle class. Most families slept in one room and lived in the other.

My Mother watched me eating at our kitchen table. It seemed to give her alternating pleasure and anxiety to watch me perform the simplest tasks.

'Don't you gobble your tea like that,' she reprimanded me.

On another occasion she might have said, 'By mind, yi've got a hunger on you today!'

I paused in shovelling homemade mince and potato pie down my throat.

'I'm not gobbling, Our Mam.'

It was Jobling's Best Scotch Mince as advertised in whitewash on his window: IF IT'S GOOD ENOUGH FOR SCOTSMEN, IT'S GOOD ENOUGH FOR YOU!

Whenever I went to the shop for a shillingsworth of mince, Mr. Jobling would ask about my Mother's well being. On receiving a glowing report, he would add an extra ounce or so of mince to the scales and ask to be remembered to her. The kindly butcher had a fondness for my Mother. I sometimes wondered what would happen if I mentioned a cough or a cold. Would he remove an ounce or two of mince from the scales?

'I didn't make that pie just for you to stuff it down your neck,' declared my Mother.

There were times when my Mother's logical processes defeated me. What else did my Mother make meat and potato pies for, d'y'think, if not for the Fergies to stuff down their necks? Tiling the kitchen floor? On occasions she would compliment me on my appetite, delighted at the speed with which I was shovelling her delectable pastry and flavoursome mince down my throat. On other days she would fret I was eating too slowly and complain I had taken against her cooking.

'I know what you're up to,' she announced.

I paused from scouring my plate clean to encounter her basilisk stare.

I protested, 'I'm not up to anything!'

'You're not going out again.'

'I don't want to.'

She quickly amended her ultimatum.

'You're not going downstairs again tonight.'

'Oh, but, Our Mam, ' I protested, 'I just want to talk to Uncle Freddie!'

'Well, I just want you in the Room, reading. You can have the Good Chair.'

Once upon a time there were two safe places in this world where no hurt could ever reach. Sharing a book on Auntie Bella's fender, or our Good Chair in the Room, reading to my Mother, while she mended a stranger's shirt cuffs. Later I would fall asleep in my bed, watching our picture gallery, purchased with cigarette coupons, flickering by firelight. *When Did You Last See Your Father? The Way Through the Bluebell Wood. Mother and Son.* While my Mother sewed her way through the darkening hours, putting small pieces of the world together again, holding my small world together.

My Mother washed my plate and I waited to dry it, sticking as ever like glue to the course of my argument.

I said, 'It was the Prince of Wales, Our Mam.'

She struck me on the head with a spoon.

'It was another daftie.'

'No, it wasn't.'

'And I say it was. Your Uncle draws them like a magnet.'

She struck me on the head with a fork to emphasise her point.

'Are you going to dry that plate or not?'

I dried the plate.

'I wish you would believe me,' I pleaded.

'Freddie's too fond of spinning you tall tales,' she said and considered whether she should hit me with a dessert spoon.

I said, 'If you're going to say I only get my just desserts, please, don't, Our Mam. You keep saying that. And that big spoon hurts.'

She gave me the spoon to dry and changed tack.

'What would he be doing here anyways?'

I was only too happy to oblige with the explanation.

'The prince borrowed a dinghy from Sir Thomas Lipton's yacht at Newcastle and rowed down to Jarrow to see the woman he loves. Only he lost an oar and we rescued him from travelling to Denmark. We nearly went with him. So you've just missed getting a postcard from Copenhagen.'

'I'd've liked that. A picture postcard. What would yis have put on it? Wish we could steer?'

My Mother was very good at jokes just when you didn't expect them.

She wiped her hands dry on the tea towel and emptied the washing up water into the slop bucket. We didn't have a tap upstairs. All water for drinking, washing, cleaning and to keep the boiler by the fire plenished had to be carried from the yard tap and soiled water returned to the yard drain.

'And this woman is Mrs. Wallace Simpson?' she enquired.

'Yes,' I answered, 'He doesn't want to be king. The crown hurts his head. Mrs. Simpson's all he ever dreamt of.'

'She's all of sixteen stone!'

'Prince Edward says she's a goddess among women,' I riposted.

My Mother took me by the shoulders and made me look her straight in the eye.

'We are talking about the same woman? Greasy Gertie? Wally Simpson's missus? Who works in the chip shop?'

I assured her, quoting the Heir To The Throne himself, 'And most wonderful of all, the Prince says, is she loves him. She truly loves him.'

My Mother released me after carefully checking behind my ears for any potato patches.

'Well, I hope Wally Simpson doesn't catch up with him. He'll do more than tattoo him. Although, mind,' she said, thoughtfully, 'Wally should be flattered somebody has an eye to his wife for more than a scoop of broken batter.'

I agreed with her, 'That's the most surprising thing of all, he says that such a wonderful woman loves him.'

My Mother flapped the tea towel at me in disbelief.

'The most surprising thing of all, is I'm listening to this nonsense. You'll have me believing it next.'

I sat down at the kitchen table.

'It's true, Our Mam.'

She put the kettle back to the fire in preparation for my Father rising for his evening meal before going to work at the bakery.

'It's nonsense. Freddie Dean did not rescue the Prince of Wales from drowning in the Tyne today.'

'Yes, he did!'

'No, he didn't!'

'Yes, he did!'

My exasperated parent came to sit beside me at the table.

'Prove it,' she said.

I pondered for a moment until inspired, I answered, 'There! You've got the mackerel right there to prove it.'

My Mother regarded the shining fish awaiting her attention.

'Of course!' she cried, 'The mackerel. I'll ask them, shall I? Which one shall I talk to first, Lecky? They all look as daft as you.'

There was no rebuttal I could summon.

She put her mouth close to my ear and said, 'Mrs. Wallace Simpson is not the Prince of Wales' fancy woman.'

While she held me by the lughole, I counterattacked with, 'Mrs. Simpson may not be fancy, but Prince Edward said, "I shall need all the strength I can summon. But I will never, ever permit us to be separated."'

I was surprised by the ferocity with which my Mother responded. I thought she was going to pull my ear from my head.

'Lecky, my idiot son! Listen to me,' she cried.

I protested, 'I could listen much better if you would let go my ear.'

She relented and let go of my ear.

'Much as I dislike the woman, you cannot go round Jarrow saying Mrs. Wallace Simpson from the fried fish shop is carrying on with the Prince of Wales.'

What could I do but defend the Heir To The Throne's honour?

'He's not carrying on with her. He's going to marry her. And nothing the Prime Minister, the bishops or you say will stop him. She is the goddess whom he adores.'

My Mother surrendered, shaking her head, bending on me a look of such sadness.

'Have it your own way. But the goddess'll have the pollis on you if you spread the joyful news round Jarrow.'

'My lips are sealed,' I responded generously.

'Good! Keep it that way. I'll have a word with your precious Uncle.'

'What word?' I asked.

'Go and wake your Dad,' she said as the thunder rolled overhead bringing a glorious summer's day to a closing crescendo.

As if on cue the kitchen door opened and my Father came in. The thunder rolling across the heavens may not have been the herald of his appearance, but it was wiser to tread warily about him when newly arisen from slumber.

My Mother said, 'Davy!'

'Accept no substitute,' he replied, yawning, lowering himself into his chair at the kitchen table. You could always hear my Father approaching. Chink, chink went the metal joint at his knee that controlled the movement of his primitive false leg, chink, chink, at every step.

'Lecky was just coming to get you,' she offered, carefully balancing his dinner plate as she closed the iron oven door, clunk.

He picked up his knife and fork as if he were about to engage in a gladiatorial combat as she placed his meal before him.

'No need,' he said, through a mouthful of mince and potato pie, 'I could hear you two going hammer and tongs.'

Raising another forkful to his face he quizzed me, 'What's the matter? You struck dumb, Lecky?'

The thunder was receding, rolling northwards for wild Northumberland, to shout defiance at the even wilder Scots beyond the Tweed. He was in a good mood. Let's not mistake the man. It's not the easiest life to spend the living day asleep and rise to find the day dying: to have missed the inconsequential chatter and irrelevant events that enliven everyday life. There is an isolation from the sunlight of family life. *Our Father, Who art in Heaven, Hallowed be Thy Name*, I prayed every night before I slept, but it wasn't God who gave us our daily bread, but Davy Ferguson, who toiled through the midnight hours at the Co-op Bakery.

'My lips are sealed, Our Dad,' I said.

'As the walrus said to the penguin,' he retorted smartly.

My Mother said, 'It's just Freddie filling his head with nonsense again.'

'It's not nonsense,' I replied, rising to my beloved Uncle's defence.'

My Father lowered the loaded fork to exclaim, indignantly, 'Hey! I thought your lips were sealed?'

'You won't believe this, Davy,' my Mother reported, 'But, apparently, the two of them rescued the Prince of Wales from drowning while they were out fishing.'

He didn't smile, but said, grudgingly, 'Well, not everybody would thank them for that.'

'But the best part is, it turns out His Royal Highness is having an affair of the heart with Mrs. Simpson from the chip shop in Connaught Terrace.'

My Father laughed out loud and the distant thunder echoed his laughter.

'You have to hand it to Freddie.'

'What, Our Dad?'

'The putty medal for prevarication.'

He shook his head in perverse admiration as he shovelled together another cartload of mince and potato pie.

'But it's all true!' I cried, 'You shouldn't laugh. In A THRONE OVER-TURNED, Archduke Michael says, 'Laugh your fill, milords, for laughter is cheap. But one day you will beg my forgiveness. For you have insulted the sweetest, dearest lady in the land.'

'Mrs. Wallace Simpson?'

'No,' I explained, 'Esmeralda the gipsy girl who tended Archduke Michael's wounds when his horse bolted in the Rheinwald Forest and he was thrown into the thicket where he lay undiscovered until he opened his eyes to view a veritable angel.'

'Where'd this happen?' my Father asked, 'The West Park?'

'No, it's in a story Auntie Bella and me are reading. But it's the same thing.'

My Father being busily engaged with a mouthful of mince and potato, my Mother corrected me, 'No, it's not. You're getting storybooks and real life mixed up.'

'I know the difference.'

The mince and potato fragmentiser suggested, 'Then mebbes Freddie doesn't.'

'Yes, he does!'

'You are talking about Freddie Dean?' my Father argued, 'The man who held the B.E.F. World record in 1917 for being blown skywards and coming back down in one piece?'

'Who held the record in 1918?' I asked.

My parents exchanged glances. My Father shook his head sadly.

He said, 'It'd be a good idea if you laid off Freddie for a bit.'

I was totally dismayed.

'But, Our Dad!' I protested.

He laid down his knife and fork on a scoured battlefield.

'You want this Scholarship?'

'But that's not.'

'Then spend more time on your long multiplication and less with Freddie.'

'I can do long multiplication.'

His face darkened.

'You think you're a bit of a professor, don't you?'

'No, I don't,' I lied.

'Yes, you do. Well, chew on this.'

I sat and looked across the table at this man who stood on one leg at a bakery table for endless aching hours, who fed the ravening ovens, burning hands and forearms, so much smooth white flesh on both limbs, to keep me fed and watered: to give me the chance to be better than he was. I never understood my Father. We shouted at one another, louder and louder as we grew older and neither of us ever listened to the other. But I was never better than he was.

He said, 'Just suppose the Prince of Wales did marry what's called a commoner. What would happen then, professor?'

'I don't know,' I answered, subdued.

'Well, I'll tell you something for nothing.'

He paused and I was grateful he wasn't going to charge me for the information. All I had was a French five centimes piece, which had been given to Mrs. Richardson in change and which she gave me to try in the Black Cat machine in Porter's shop. Unfortunately it stuck in the slot. Fortunately Mrs. Porter gave it me back before she realised it was a French coin and that I wasn't French.

'Are you listening to me, Lecky?' my Father threatened.

'Yes, Our Dad,' I said, 'You were going to tell me something for nothing. I've only got five centimes anyway. And it's bent.'

He looked at my Mother and she shook her head.

'People kow-tow to Mr. and Mrs. Windsor because they think they're someat special. If they found out the truth, the whole pack of them'd get the Order of the Boot.'

'Well, then the Prince of Wales could run off with Mrs. Simpson and live happily ever after.'

That seemed a satisfactory solution to me.

'The state we're in now,' he said solemnly, 'it would be the crowning touch for this country if the young King deserted his post. With Herr Hitler shouting the odds, it would be curtains for Old England.'

'I didn't know Hair Hitler did curtains,' I said. I knew he'd been a house painter, but I didn't know he dabbled in soft furnishings.

He persisted in his explanation; little was I aware that we were alike as two pears from the same tree.

'The last thing we need is a morganatic marriage. D'y'know what that means, professor?'

'No.'

He regarded me with satisfaction.

'Then look it up in your dictionary.'

He rose from the table, kissed my Mother on the cheek, complimented her, with 'Smashing! Top hole!' and left our modest stage with unheard applause ringing in his ears, chink, chink!

Seven

WE LISTENED IN SILENCE TO HIS PROGRESS, chink, chink, down the stairs and the latch lifting on the bottom passage door into the yard. There he would wash and splash at the yard tap like a Spartan, summer or winter, bare to the waist, the fading tattoo of the bugle and the star on the back of his left shoulder receiving proper attention from the fat bar of Carbolic soap. He was one of the dwindling band of men who had marched under the bugle and the star of the Cameronians, the second battalion that called itself the Scottish Rifles. They wore the tattoo so they could more easily identify their dead.

My Mother drew hot water from the fireside boiler to wash his plate and cutlery. I stood by with the tea towel to briskly polish the little chinamen on our willow pattern plate. In the sunlit evening the rumble of distant thunder stirred us to speech.

I asked, 'Then it would be a really bad thing if The Prince of Wales was enamoured of Mrs. Simpson?'

'If,' said my Mother, 'and it's a big if, if the Prince of Wales were enamelled of Mrs. Wallace Simpson it would be the worst thing all round. But then he isn't really, is he?'

I didn't meet her eye, but bent to the task of polishing off the little chinamen.

The distant thunder rumbled as echoes of artillery long since silenced. I have one enduring image of my Father, a company runner during the Battle of Passchendaele, stumbling, falling, getting up and running on through shot and shell, from here to hell and back again, carrying messages between his company and headquarters, the one surviving runner in his division. Men would shake hands or touch his collar for luck. On ran brave Davy, through barrages beyond bearing, until his luck deserted him.

As a special treat I was allowed to take my slice of apple pie into the Room to eat to keep my Mother company. Sitting in the Good Chair, scanning the dictionary, nibbling my Mother's delectable pastry oozing with sweet apple syrup, while she worked at her sewing machine was heaven indeed. The Singer sang chuckle, chuckle as my Mother worked the treadle. The only fly in the ointment of our well-being was the meaning of 'morganatic' as offered by the dictionary.

I interrupted the chatter of the machine, chuckle, chuckle, to say, 'This doesn't make much sense, Our Mam.'

The sewing machine, chuckle, hesitated and stopped.

'What doesn't?' she asked.

'The dictionary. "Morganatic: otherwise called lefthanded, and common in German principalities, concerning a dubious liaison with a lady of inferior rank."'

'Yes?'

'You're morganatic.'

'Always the ready compliment,' said she.

'No,' I explained, 'You're left-handed.'

Snipping a thread she added, 'And a lady of inferior rank into the bargain. Thank you very much.'

I hastened to reassure her.

'You're not inferior. You're superior.'

My Mother laughed.

'Well, you have looked it up,' she agreed, 'So I'll tell you what I know. Mind, I wasn't the best scholar in the class.'

I encouraged her.

'Go on, Our Mam!'

She toyed with the sewing machine handle for a moment and then said, 'I was told when he was the Prince of Wales, King George secretly married Mrs. Morgan.'

The perfect crust of my Mother's apple tart fell to the plate from my nerveless hand. Obviously then, it was a regular feature of royal life, young princes of the blood, taking up with Jarrow matrons.

My Mother added, 'It was all hushed up, of course.'

I nodded agreement whilst salvaging my crust. I never knew anyone who made a better crust than my Mother. It was not something to discard, but a pleasure to enjoy.

'Or else they'd get the Order of the Boot,' I confirmed.

My Mother continued, 'The entry in the church register was torn out.'

'That's sacrilege!'

'And Mrs. Morgan was comfortably settled so she wouldn't cause a fuss.'

My Mother rather impressed with her own erudition began to pedal her treadle, chuckle, chuckle, bowing her head to her work, chuckle, chuckle

I knew to whom my Mother was referring. Mrs. Morgan was the licensee of the Prince of Wales pub on the corner of Ellison Street and Grange Road. I remembered passing this portly woman in purple standing in the pub doorway, fragrant with the scent of old ale and tobacco, and my Mother saying to Auntie Bella, 'Well, we know how she got that, don't we!'

As I savoured the last of my apple pie crust my Mother raised her head from her sewing to worry, 'I hope the Grammar School'll not be bothered you know it all before you start.'

I reassured her it would not be so.

'I'll pretend I don't know,' I answered and she bent her head to her work again, chuckle, chuckle.

To have a son at Jarrow Grammar School was her heart's desire and what it presaged, her dearest dream: her son a railway clerk. Whenever we crossed the bridge at Jarrow station, often gifted with a cloud of steam and sulphurous smoke, we exchanged secret smiles of anticipation.

There were two butcher shops in Albert Road, Jobling's and McAtominey's. We used Jobling's, as the butcher was sweet on my Mother.

The heart does not choose its own butcher as the poet didn't say. So the day I went into Jobling's while my Mother walked on to the Co-op and the amiable butcher came forward to greet his customer with his customary smile, my conscience was uneasy.

'Hello, young man,' said Mr. Jobling, 'I haven't seen you. Or your Mam for weeks now. Where've you been hiding yourselves?'

I said, 'We've haven't been hiding, Mr. Jobling. "Time drives our paths apart" as the poet says.'

I smiled a false smile. Judas Iscariot would've been proud of me.

Mr. Jobling smiled a relieved smile.

'I thought you'd given up on me. Or that your Mam was off-colour? Is she keeping well? Your Mam? Nothing untoward, I hope?'

If I'd told him I'd recently started taking our custom down the road to MacAtominey's, ducking down as I passed before his window, it would've broken his generous heart and we'd never have had another free ham shank for soup. Love laughs at butchers as well as locksmiths.

'How is your Mam? Keeping well?'

'Very well, thank you, Mr, Jobling,' I answered cheerily, 'She sends her best regards, hoping to find you in the pink.'

The genial butcher flushed pink himself at the compliment, but replied, 'In the red as ever, unfortunately. But what can I do for you today?'

'What Our Mam would like,' I suggested, 'is a shillingsworth of your best mince, please, but I've only got tenpence.'

I placed ten pennies on the counter, leaving two in my pocket and looked soulfully up at our friendly flesher. Oliver Twist could've taken lessons from me.

'Well, we shall have to see what we can do, won't we?'

Mr. Jobling slapped fresh mince upon the scales as generously as a drunken bricklayer with mortar.

'How's that?' he declared, 'As the bowler said to the cloth cap.'

I asked timidly, 'Is that tenpence?'

Mr. Jobling smiled upon me as the sun upon the righteous.

'To you, young man, that's ten pence.'

'Thank you very much.'

You mustn't think for one moment that although I behaved very badly with Mr. Jobling, that I kept my Mother's tuppence. I would put the plump newspaper parcel down on the kitchen table and then slap down the two pennies change.

'Is your Mam going to St. Thomas's picnic?' asked the butcher casually.

'She never misses,' I assured him.

'Be sure and tell her I'm chief steward this year.'

'She was busy all last night on her sewing machine,' I confirmed truthfully, and, untruthfully, 'She wondered if you'd be chief steward this year.'

The bemused butcher mused for a moment.

I breathed a short prayer for forgiveness as I'd recently discovered in an unpleasant interview with Miss Madison that the Commandment about *not bearing false witness* was actually about not telling lies which was news to me. I had wondered why God had not included telling lies in His Commandments, but concluded that He knew telling lies is often kinder than the truth.

'She's always well turned out, your Mam,' said the musing butcher, 'Would she fancy a handful of sweetbreads, d'y'think?'

'If you asked Our Mam what she liked best, she'd say a handful of sweetbreads, please, every time,' I agreed enthusiastically.

'Lightly poached in a little milk with a shaving of onion, sweetbreads is a feast fit for a Queen,' he enthused rhapsodically, eyes alight, his breast heaving under his bloody apron. In such words does a butcher declare undying love.

I agreed, 'That's just how she does them.'

'Then she shall have them!' cried Mr. Jobling, bustling off to wherever he hid his sweetbreads and other fleshly dainties, returning to request, 'You'll give her my best wishes, won't you, young man?'

As he wrapped the sweetbreads, I replied with equal enthusiasm, 'I will and she always asks after you. When I go in, the first thing she'll say is, How was Mr. Jobling to-day?'

It seemed to me that as he handed over my purchases, my benefactor blushed.

'Mr. Jobling?'

'Yes, young man?'

'Would you have anything for our dog?'

My Mother was never aware of this fantasy romance, which I fanned so furiously on her behalf. At St. Thomas's picnic, Mr. Jobling'd stand ten feet away all afternoon, blissfully happy, hoping she'd invite him to join her, but as she didn't know, she never did. Ah, the pangs, the pangs, the pangs of unrequited love! Mr. Jobling came to her funeral and wept, which surprised everybody but me because I knew he loved my Mother. He brought enough pigs' feet to feed an army.

When I confessed all to Uncle Freddie he pondered awhile and asked, 'Was the man happy in his delusion?'

I answered, 'He was very generous with the mince and sweetbreads.'

'Enough said,' my Uncle replied, 'You've done little mischief. In fact, you may have performed a miracle and created happiness.'

Going to MacAtominey's was a different pan of pease pudden. When I hung back from being served Mr. MacAtominey asked, 'Do you just come in to smell the meat? Or d'y'want serving?'

I said, 'I was being polite letting the lady get served.'

The good butcher regarded me with the same glance he would give a dodgy pork pie.

'There's been a regiment through the shop while you're dodging about.'

'I'm just being polite.'

My problem was I had fallen madly in love with the butcher's daughter. Her hair was as red as fire and her eyes as green as the sea and her name was Charlotte MacAtominey.

Her Father said, 'I cannot have you shuffling about kicking up the sawdust. This is not a public waiting room. Do you want serving or don't you?'

'I want serving.'

'Hallelujah!'

'What I'd like, Mr. MacAtominey, please,' I replied, 'is a shillingsworth of your best mince, but I've only got tenpence.'

'Then you shall have tenpennorth of my mince.'

'Best mince,' I affirmed.

'All my mince is best mince,' said Mr. MacAtominey.

'In that case,' I surrendered, 'I'll have a shillingsworth of your best mince.'

'Happy days are here again,' this sarcastic butcher informed me.

Charlotte MacAtominey was the Greta Garbo of the Grange Ward. She could wrestle and climb and spit for miles. She lived on rollerskates and she'd fly down the pavement holding onto a cart, with her heartbreaking hair streaming behind her, and the driver'd never threaten her with his whip because she was a goddess with hair as red as fire and eyes as green as the sea.

'You still here?' asked Mr. MacAtominey, returning to the shop to find me still on the premises, 'Look, son, the way it works is, you get served and then you leave the shop.'

I had been communing with the bull's head on the wall.

'Is that bull's head real, Mr. MacAtominey?'

'Yes, it's real.'

'Is it dead?'

'Yes, it's dead.'

'Is it just the head or is the body the other side of the wall?'

The idea was to hang about the shop as long as possible in case Charlotte appeared. The family lived upstairs and I knew Norman Richardson had been in to play. I prayed the delightful Charlotte would appear at the back of the shop and she'd see me and her green eyes would light up with pleasure and she'd ask me in to play.

'I was just wondering, Mr. MacAtominey, is the sawdust fresh every day?' I enquired.

'We lay fresh sawdust every day.'

I ventured, 'Do you chop up the trees yourself?'

'Will you leave the pork pies alone? Somebody's got to eat them when you've finished poking them about.'

My putative future Father-in-law wasn't an easy man to make conversation with, but I was doing my best. With one eye on the back of the shop and one eye on his handy cleaver.

'Have you no home to go to, son?' he asked, striving to keep patience.

'I'm doing a composition for school,' I explained, 'Entitled *A Day in the*

Life of a Pork Pie. I'm finding out about it.'

'Have you come to play with Charlotte?'

'I thought I might do *My Life as a Black Pudden*,' I countered.

'She's not here. Charlotte's away to see her granny.'

Darkened was my day, my hopes downcast.

'Her black puddens were famous from Billingham to Berwick,' I pronounced.

'Yi've a fancy for a good black pudden, have yi?' suggested Mr. MacAtominey, somewhat surprised.

'When will she be back, Mr. MacAtominey?'

'That I cannot say. Our Charlie's a law unto herself.'

'Oh! Right.'

Reluctantly I moved to the door.

'Who shall I say called?' asked the master of sarcasm.

'Nobody. I'm not anybody in particular.'

'Don't forget your mince, Mr. Nobody.'

Eight

'I'VE BEEN SWORN TO SILENCE,' I said to Uncle Freddie, 'But you haven't explained what I've been sworn to silence for.'

We were sitting on a bench in the new park watching the labourers who moved as rarely as possible to ensure the job lasted as long as possible. They were known as the Statues in the Park. The squirrels that decorated the cast iron ends of the park benches were livelier than these men.

'The intention of swearing someone to silence,' said my Uncle Freddie, 'is to silence them from asking any unnecessary questions.'

That morning I had stepped out of our netty into the morning sunshine to find my Uncle leaving by the back yard door.

Without breaking step he had said, 'You are sworn to silence. Follow me.'

Aware of my Father's warning to spend less time with Uncle Freddie I looked up at our kitchen window, but there was no one visible to deny me. I followed my Uncle out into the back lane.

'Where are we going?' I asked.

'Sworn to silence,' he said and we marched off briskly together.

Where we were going was to a bench in the park where we sat and watched the fortunate labourers spinning out their tasks.

Suddenly Uncle Freddie rose to his feet.

'I wasn't sure he'd turn up,' he said.

'Who?' I asked.

In reply my Uncle raised a hand in salute to the person approaching us through the spinney.

'The Prince of Wales!' I breathed, answering my own question.

He was wearing proper trousers this time, a suit of Harris tweed, alas, the same ridiculous dinner plate cap, and wielding a natty silver-headed cane with which he was carelessly beheading the nurtured blossoms through which he was striding. KEEP OFF THE GRASS held no meaning for the Heir To The Throne. He was the very image of the young Squire in TOWERING FALL who loses every penny of his inheritance in the gambling hells of London and returns, the prodigal son, to his Father's estate to work as a simple labourer for bed and bread and then gets lockjaw. The family think he's sulking so they ignore him and he dies.

'Freddie!' he cried as he approached, 'And Lackey too! Capital! I hope I haven't kept you chaps waiting, eh?'

'Not at all,' said my Uncle, disregarding the thirty minutes we'd spent sitting on the park bench. They shook hands warmly with one another, and the Prince tousled my hair, which is a very irritating habit of adults.

'D'y'know, Freddie?' said the Prince.

'No, sir. What do I know?'

'I was watching these chaps.'

He indicated the slothlike labourers with his cane. This is a habit common to Royalty: they all point at things with stick or parasol.

'And I thought, Freddie, old bun, how wonderful to be able to lean on a hoe and contemplate the world,' he sighed, 'Such simple pleasures are denied to kings and princes.'

'Sir,' said Uncle Freddie, but his interruption was unnoticed.

'Freddie, old friend, I'd give everything I own, co-respondent shoes, gold toothbrush, diamond tiepin, every privilege of rank, to be able to lean upon my hoe and contemplate the wonders of the natural world as these simple sons of the soil do.'

'What about Mrs. Simpson?' I asked.

'Perhaps we could find two hoes, eh?' he mused, 'And stand together contemplating nature, two soul mates bound by unseen bonds, in touch with a world beyond mere artifice.'

'I don't think Mrs. Simpson,' I warned, 'is one for leaning on hoes and contemplating Artifice or anywhere else.'

Uncle Freddie intervened to say, 'Sir, what you are looking at isn't what it seems. Employment is like gold dust in Jarrow. These men have a few weeks work arranged by the Council. They're trying to make the jobs last and to leave a few more weeks work for other unemployed men. But it isn't real work. These men aren't sons of the soil. Among them there's draughtsmen, shipwrights, boilermakers, carpenters. Any manner of men. Skilled men. Educated men. Humiliated by this farce.'

'D'y'know, Freddie,' said the Prince of Wales, 'You're absolutely right. I introduced myself to one chap and, bless me, if he wasn't the King of Albania!'

'What a coincidence!' remarked my Uncle, 'Birds of a feather!'

'When I asked him why he'd given up his throne he told me he preferred his personal freedom.'

The Prince of Wales sighed deeply, 'Stout fellow! Brothers under the skin, what? I told him I too wished to be free to lean upon a hoe. He said I could borrow his hoe anytime and he would snatch forty winks under the trees. How kind! But, of course, I couldn't deprive him.'

The Prince smiled wryly and Uncle Freddie and I exchanged glances of pure bafflement.

'Now you promised me, Freddie, you'd show me the game they play in Jarrow? With the sacks?'

'Oh, yes!' said my Uncle, 'Fun on the pit heap! Top hole!'

As we walked Uncle Freddie tried to explain to the Prince the absurdity of arranged employment.

'In eighteen forty eight,' said my Uncle, 'In the revolution in France they tried much the same game.'

'That's not the revolution where they cut off everybody's head, but the Scarlet Pimpernel saved heaps and heaps of Dukes and Duchesses?'

'No,' said my Uncle, 'They cut back on cutting off heads this time round.'

I added, 'The Scarlet Pimpernel wasn't real. He's in a story.'

'Really?' said His Royal Highness, 'Are you sure? In a story?'

'What the revolutionary committee did to create employment,' said Uncle Freddie pressing on with his self-imposed task of educating Royalty, 'was to hire men at a shilling a day to dig holes in the Champs de Mars. The next day a different band of labourers filled in the holes at the same price. And so they continued, digging and filling.'

The Prince stopped dead in his tracks.

'What a wonderful idea! You have solved the unemployment problem at a stroke, Freddie! Would you like to become my personal financial adviser? I guarantee an excellent salary.'

Uncle Freddie turned a glance of despair upon me.

To the Prince, he said, slowly, calmly, 'But don't you see, sir?'

'See what?'

'It wasn't very long before they ran out of shillings,' I said.

'Then we'd pay them in sixpences,' said the Prince.

On the slagheap there were perhaps a dozen or more men and boys, dragging sacks, combing the waste for scraps of coal. Here and there were burrows where men had dug their own drift mines into the mountain seeking waste coal from earlier years as the surface supply dried up. These were death traps waiting to be sprung because although the galleries were boarded with waste wood the composition of the slagheap was unsure and liable to collapse after rain. Yet still desperate men tunnelled into the heart of the slag hunting out waste coal rejected by previous generations.

We watched the scavengers working the slagheap, scraping away with homemade rakes for the tiniest scrap of coal. Their interest in us had vanished as soon as they were assured we were not the police.

'What are they collecting?' asked the Prince.

'Scrapings,' my Uncle replied, 'Coal. Scrapings of coal.'

'Should we not borrow a sack and join in?' the Prince enquired of my Uncle, 'It looks good fun.'.

'I think not, sir,' my Uncle commenced, but the Heir To The Throne interrupted, 'Look here, Freddie, we're chums, are we not?'

'I suppose so, sir.'

'Then you must call me David,' announced the Prince, 'I much prefer David to Edward.'

Yet another eccentricity of Royalty! If they liked a name better than their own, apparently they simply adopted the new name.

'As you wish, David,' Uncle Freddie said hesitantly.

'Splendid, Freddie!' cried the Prince, 'Then we really are chums!'

I wondered what my Mother would say if I announced that in future I wished to be called Nebuchadnezzar which I considered the most glorious of names. Or Nezzie for short?

'I'd rather like a go at collecting scrapings,' said our new friend David, 'In South Africa. At Joburg for a lark we went out where they dumped the waste from the gold mines, and do you know, within five minutes, I had a handful of gold nuggets! I spotted them! Just lying there on the ground! It was such jolly fun!'

'It's not quite the same here,' Uncle Freddie said, and as if on cue, a whistle blew and then another and another.

Across the slope of the slag heap a line of police constables appeared followed by an Inspector. At the sight of the constabulary the coal pickers began to run, the stronger among them dragging their sacks, the weaker releasing their burdens to run faster. Where the constables caught up with the coal scratchers they began to beat them with their truncheons and when they fell down they kicked the old men. I felt Uncle Freddie tense with anger.

'Oh, I say! Bad show!' cried The Heir To The Throne.

The Inspector blew his whistle and the beatings ceased. The old men limped away. The Inspector approached us.

'Congratulations, Inspector Elliott!' my Uncle called to him, 'Another wicked crime detected and punished!'

The constables retraced their steps, emptying out the discarded sacks, so that the men could not return to retrieve their pickings.

Inspector Elliott came to us, and fixed his ferrety eyes on Uncle Freddie.

'I know you, Freddie Dean.'

'And I know you, Inspector Elliott,' retorted my Uncle.

'But who's this with you then? I don't know him.'

'If I told you he's the Prince of Wales, you wouldn't believe me.'

The Prince had the good sense to remain silent. The Inspector snorted his laughter. He called to the constables, 'Here's a right one. The Prince of Wales!'

The constables came to stare at the Heir To The Throne.

'Do you know it's an offence to impersonate Royalty?' the Inspector enquired.

'Do you know,' said the Prince of Wales, 'that it is an offence for the constables to behave as I have just seen them behave? And an even greater offence for you as their Inspector to permit them to do so? A very bad show!'

Uncle Freddie and I stared at one another in astonishment.

The senior constable stepped forward and thrust his pig's snout under the Prince's nose.

'How would it be, sir, if you was to stumble on this uneven ground and I was to fall over you accidentally while I was helping you up?'

I felt Uncle Freddie tense himself to intervene, but the Inspector was more circumspect and stepped forward to say, 'You gentlemen are trespassing on private property. If you do not remove yourselves immediately, I will arrest you.'

We turned away from the policemen, but when I looked back Inspector Elliott was looking after us thoughtfully – if a ferret can ever be considered thoughtful.

'I think you've got him worried, David,' I said, 'It'll be the silver handle on your stick. Or your cap. He won't ever have seen a cap like yours.'

'A very bad show,' said the Prince, 'Absolutely bad show!'

We regarded our chum David with new-won respect.

On the way home we stopped at Simpson's chip shop and bought a pennorth of chips that we shared on the pavement. During the time we were in the shop and eating on the pavement Mrs Wallace Simpson and the Prince of Wales never blinked an eye at one another. This to me was conclusive proof. I know the cunning ways of love. In A THRONE OVERTURNED, Archduke Michael never blinks an eye as the gipsy maid Esmeralda is savagely tortured with red-hot irons before his very eyes rather than reveal that the wretch in the jester's suit, singing and dancing to amuse the usurper Harold, is the man they seek.

The Prince asked, 'If they do get the scrapings home what do they do with them?'

Uncle Freddie was perplexed for a moment.

'Do with them?'

'Yes. What do they do with the coal scrapings?'

Uncle Freddie said, 'They burn them. It may be the poorest coal, but it burns. They use it to cook food, wash the bairns, heat the house.'

'Don't they have radiators?' asked the Prince With Two Names.

Nine

'HE IS,' SAID MY UNCLE FREDDIE as we turned into Hurworth Place back lane, 'a perfect example of the witless wonder of the nobility, unknowing of the real world. But how can you know anything of the world if there's a servant to hold your drawers open for you to step into and another to hold one's elbow lest one should lose one's balance. And another to fasten your trouser buttons.'

'And one to put your cap on?'

'Undoubtedly,' he said, 'But the one thing he isn't is a coward. And that counts for a great deal. It might be the saving of him yet. But he doesn't know how close he came to being knocked down and having his teeth kicked in.'

With his hand on the latch of our backyard door he said, 'So if you don't see me for a few days you'll know why.'

'Why?' I said.

'I'll be trying to educate our chum David as to the ways of this weary world.'

'And save him having his front teeth kicked in.' I confirmed.

'That too,' he said, 'But mebbes I can knock some sense into him. So mum's the word!'

'My lips are sealed!' I cried.

We used a large basket with two handles to deliver the laundry washed, dried, mended and ironed by my Mother and Auntie Bella to their clients. A piece of bed sheet lined the basket so the wickerwork didn't mark or snag the linen. In the sanctuary of her kitchen Auntie Bella was finishing the ironing and I was filling the basket, making a note of every item because some of the ladies they washed for were not above accusing my Mother and Auntie Bella of stealing the odd pillow slip. I was trying to acquaint my Auntie of my pressing anxiety while unfortunately she seemed similarly preoccupied.

Ticking off pillow cases with the indelible pencil, I asked, 'So what should I do, Auntie Bella?'

She returned an iron to the fire and hesitated for a moment.

'About what, pet?'

I felt I didn't really have her attention.

'About what I was telling you.'

Auntie Bella spat on the hot iron and it sizzled its readiness. She returned to ironing, swiftly, precisely.

'What were you telling me?'

'About, y'know,' I said. It hurt too much to repeat the words.

Auntie Bella said, 'There should be fourteen pillow slips.'

I stopped and looked at her.

'You weren't listening, were you?'

To my chagrin Auntie Bella returned the iron to the hob and picked up a newspaper from her chair.

'Lecky,' she said, 'I want you to have a look at this picture.'

On the front page of the newspaper there was a blurred photograph of a group of men. In the centre of the group was the Prince of Wales.

I said, 'At least he's got proper trousers on.'

'Never you mind trousers!'

I read from the caption under the photograph.

"Sir Thomas Lipton and his guest, the Prince of Wales, at Newcastle Guildhall with the Mayor and dignitaries."

'Now,' said Auntie Bella, 'Take a good look at the man standing next to the Prince of Wales. Does he remind you of anybody?'

'Charlie Chaplin?'

Auntie Bella flapped me with the folded newspaper.

'Look again,' she said.

'A bit like Uncle Freddie?'

Auntie Bella peered again at the newspaper.

'He said he had a few days labouring for Harrison's,' Auntie Bella suggested, doubtfully, 'but I was to keep mum.'

'He told me to keep mum,' I added truthfully.

I was waltzing on thin ice having been sworn to silence.

She said, 'It does look like him. Thinner. But if it's Freddie what's he doing there?'

'It could be an accident. He could just be passing by and stopped when they were taking the photograph,' I suggested, 'Granny and Grandad Fergie are on the postcard in McKay's shop window walking on Shields pier. They didn't mean to be.'

'Not the same thing at all,' my Auntie countered.

'Well, if it is Uncle Freddie I hope he's telling the Prince to give up his pointless passion for Mrs. Simpson and save the Throne despite the heart ache it will cause him. Otherwise it'll be curtains for Old England.'

Auntie Bella turned again to her ironing.

She decided, 'I can't believe it's Freddie.'

She ironed an unfortunate nightgown with unnecessary vigour.

'He's too tall for Freddie. Besides your Uncle has a very common face when you look at it.'

I was rather relieved I was not an item for ironing.

'But he does look uncannily like Freddie.'

A shirt received the same drastic treatment.

'I shall keep the paper and ask Freddie when I catch up with him.'

The last shirt was ironed more thoughtfully.

'That's what I shall do,' said my Auntie, 'Now what was it you were saying, pet?'

'My heart's broken into a hundred pieces, Auntie Bella,' I confessed.

'Oh, lamb!' she cried, 'What on earth has happened?'

'Norman Richardson has been invited to Charlotte MacAtominey's birthday party,' I lamented, 'And I haven't.'

'Shush, shush!' she comforted me, 'That isn't the end of world, pet!'

'Oh, yes, it is!' I cried, 'I wanted to die a hero's death, and now I'm going to die of a broken heart.'

I was inconsolable despite Auntie Bella's best efforts with hugs, kisses and Little Gem biscuits. I was so glad that Uncle Freddie wasn't there to see me in such distress. Thankful that my Father was sound asleep upstairs because his icy contempt for such weak-kneed behaviour would've shrivelled my soul beyond salvation. Even my Mother would've threatened me direly, probably with *"I'll give you birthday parties"* when it was self-evident that I wasn't going to any such festivity. She would've drummed a tattoo on my skull with a spoon to bring me to my senses. But not my Auntie Bella who had an endless warmth of heart, a richness of comfort to offer when in everyday reality she was of the poorest estate.

My Auntie Bella is the one person I know who in a lifetime never did any harm. She endured war and separation, the tragedy of childlessness, the misery of the Thirties, worked endlessly with little reward and yet lived placidly, forever hopeful, forgiving and free from malice.

'I'll tell you what to do, pet,' Auntie Bella decided, 'Like I'm going to do with Freddie when he turns up. Ask him. Go and ask Norman how he got invited to the party.'

Norman Richardson must've known I was coming because his backyard door was bolted. I could hear his babyish voice and other voices so he had boys in to play with him. Norman didn't play in the street. He had friends in to play. I banged on the backyard door.

'Open this door, Norman Richardson,' I shouted.

There was silence and then giggling, whispering and shuffling.

'I know you're in there and I know who you've got with you.'

'Wha'd'y'want?' asked Norman's muffled voice.

I said, reasonably, 'I want to talk to you, that's all.'

'You're not coming in.'

'I don't want to play in your backyard.'

'I wouldn't have you in to play.'

Less reasonably I shouted, 'I wouldn't play in your backyard if you paid me. Your drains stink. Just open the door and I won't come over the step. Promise! I just want to ask you something.'

There was again whispering and giggling as Norman and friends discussed this offer.

Norman Richardson was a boy who was rich enough to buy his friends because his Mother entertained a dozen uncles a month. When, in my innocence, I suggested a similar arrangement to my Mother, she held my head under the yard tap and scoured my mouth with carbolic soap.

Norman whimpered, 'I know you, Lecky Fergie. You'd only bash iss up.'

'Honest,' I cried, 'I'm not gona bash you up, I promise.'

There was muttering behind the door.

'I know that's what I said last time,' I admitted, 'But this is different.'

A man leading a horse and cart passed by me in the lane. I waited until he'd gone.

'All right, don't open the door,' I surrendered. 'I'll talk to you through the door.'

A muffled Norman said, 'Wha'd'y'want?'

'Just telliss, Norman, how you got invited to Charlotte McAtominey's party? If you tell iss, the next time Uncle Freddie and me go fishing, you can come as well.'

Well, I knew that promise was safe. Mrs. Richardson wouldn't let her little prince go out in a smelly, leaky boat on that nasty wet sea. But the answer I received was not what I had expected.

Through the door Norman Richardson said, 'I got a personal invitation through the post with a proper stamp, but anybody can go that brings a present.'

I was stunned. A personal invitation!

'You're a liar, Norman! Charlotte MacAtominey's not like that. She'd never have a party like that. Anybody can go who brings a present? Never! I don't believe you!'

Sadly I did believe him. There was a flavour about bring-a-present-parties that was sour on the tongue, but the bitter potion was that Norman Richardson had received a personal invitation from Charlotte. Through the door I said, 'D'y'know what I'm doing now, Norman?'

The steady drumming of the stream of urine on the back door and the penetration of the golden inundation below the backyard door into the yard brought cries of dismay and disgust that were music to my ears.

'Too late, Norman. You can't stop me. I've been saving it up for ages,' I cried, 'You can't tell your Mammy. She's upstairs telling Uncle Arthur's fortune. I can see the curtains drawn.'

It had been a bitter blow to discover Norman Richardson had been personally invited to Charlotte MacAtominey's party. And not much consolation to discover it was a pay-as-you-go do. But I had to go at whatever cost. All I needed was the wonderful gift that would win me Charlotte McAtominey's heart. But first I had to undertake a certain errand the success of which would determine the future of Old England.

Unfortunately my mission was not quite an unqualified success; the aftermath of which had left me standing in the Room on a sheet of newspaper while a battle had raged about my head. The battlefield was silent now and the victor departed.

'Don't you dare move off that newspaper!' cried my Mother.

'I wasn't going to,' I offered unhappily.

'Well,' she said, somewhat flustered, ' I hope I never have to go through anything like that again.'

'I thought she was hanging on for her tea.'

'The place smells like a chip shop. What on earth possessed you?'

'She's squashed that cushion flatter than a pancake.'

'Don't you try to distract me! If your Dad hears about this visitation you won't look much better.'

'He was the one that told me about the curtains and Old England.'

'I don't think this is quite what he meant,' she retorted angrily, 'I cannot believe you did what she says you did. I've never been so embarrassed.'

'All I did was plead with Mrs. Simpson to give up her hopeless love for the Prince of Wales whatever the personal heartbreak.'

My Mother sat down in the Good Chair and shook her head sadly, 'I don't know whether to laugh or cry.'

Emboldened I said, 'I warned her if she ran away with Prince Edward that would be the end of Old England. I said, do you want to have the whole country on your conscience, Mrs. Simpson, just to satisfy your illicit passion?'

'You walked into Simpson's chip shop and said that?'

'I practised it first outside.'

'But why?' my Mother persisted.

'Somebody had to do it.'

She sighed deeply.

'Of course, it had to be you. My son.'

'I waited my turn like everybody else.'

I thought for a moment that she was going to laugh, but I was mistaken.

'Don't tell me there was a queue?'

'I told her, she'd end up with a pub like Mrs. Morgan, smelling of beer and baccy. A chip shop's much nicer. You don't have people fighting and being sick. Well, not all the time.'

'What did she say?'

'That's when she hit me on the head with the chip basket. That's why I'm covered in grease and batter.'

'Oh, Lecky,' she said, 'What am I going to do with you? Apart from getting you bathed. You're sliding on the downward path, my son, and I don't only blame the chip fat.'

I defended myself, saying, 'I was only thinking of Old England.'

'I'll give you Old England,' my Mother threatened, 'Not another word! Go and drag the bath upstairs. Let's get you sorted out.'

Of course, this bathetic incident only confirmed my worst fears. I didn't doubt Prince Edward's declaration of love and Mrs. Simpson's reaction certainly convinced me. Why else would she threaten if she heard another squeak, 'somebody' would be round. Would that certain 'somebody's' initials happen to be H.R.H., d'y'think? Would it be Beefeaters and halberds at dawn? As I went down our stairs to get the zinc bath from the nail in the yard wall I thought I heard my Mother laughing, but I must have been mistaken.

Ten

My Mother was working peacefully at her sewing machine when an anxious Bella came to interrupt.

'Have you seen the Chronicle?' my Auntie Bella asked.

'If Our Lecky's got himself in print, I'll kill him.'

My Auntie Bella shook her head.

'No. It's this picture. There!'

My Mother took the newspaper from her sister, scanned the photograph and read the caption.

'Sir Thomas Lipton and party visit Palmer's site. The Prince of Wales says, "Something must be done",' she recited, 'Again? He must have it written on the back of his hand. So?'

Auntie Bella suggested, 'Look at the photograph.'

'I'm looking.'

'Who does the man behind the Prince of Wales remind you of?'

My Mother scanned the poorly printed picture again.

'It can't be Freddie? Can it?'

'You tell me.'

It was then my Mother heard my footsteps on the landing and the afternoon took a very different turn.

'Lecky? Is that you?'

'I won't be in for tea,' I called cheerily.

'Get yourself in here, ' she replied.

Reluctantly I entered the Room to face the two women.

My Mother asked, 'What're you up to?'

Auntie Bella said, surprised, 'You've brushed your hair. I've never known you do that before.'

My Mother repeated, 'What're you up to?'

'I'm going to Charlotte McAtominey's party.'

Auntie Bella was thrilled.

'Oh, I'm so glad you're going! That's why you've brushed your hair. It must be love!'

'No!' I protested.

My Mother was of a less sentimental turn of mind.

'What've you got behind your back?'

'Nothing,' I lied.

Auntie Bella stepped to one side.

'Yes, you have, Lecky.'

'Show me,' ordered the grimfaced matron who used to be my Mother.

What I had behind my back was Granny's solitary knick-knack from the kitchen mantelpiece; five little ivory elephants marching over an ebony bridge. The first thing I remember in my life is five little ivory elephants marching.

'Only this,' I said and held it out to my Mother who said, 'What're you doing with Granny's elephants?'

There was a terrible silence in the Room. Never in my life before did I think silence had weight, but now I was being crushed under the burden.

Auntie Bella broke the silence, but the weight remained on my shoulders.

Sadly, she said, 'You were going to give them to Charlotte MacAtominey. Weren't you?'

'Come on,' said my Mother, 'Speak up like a man!'

The ebony bridge was burning my hand.

'I was going to give them to Charlotte MacAtominey for her birthday.'

My Mother sighed and asked, 'Didn't you think I'd notice they were missing? Or didn't you care?'

The desperation was loud in my voice.

'I've got to have a present to give her. I just have to.'

Auntie Bella said with surprising gentleness, 'But not by stealing Granny's elephants, surely? She has so little.'

'You don't understand.'

'Go and put the elephants back on the mantelpiece,' my Mother ordered.

'I have to have a present,' I urged.

'If she's any sort of a girl,' Auntie Bella said, 'she's not invited you just to get a present.'

'You don't understand.'

My Mother said, 'Don't keep saying, you don't understand. You might think we're dafties, but we're not so dusty.'

I begged her.

'Please let me give her the elephants.'

'Go and put the elephants back.'

'I haven't got anything to give her.'

My Mother said, 'Yes, you have. You. Your self.'

I shook my head sadly.

'She wouldn't want me.'

'Well, she's not getting Granny's elephants,' she decided, 'Give them here.'

Reluctantly I surrendered the elephants.

'I hope you're both very pleased. You've ruined my life. I'm not going to the party now.'

I turned to go, but Auntie Bella caught me.

'Lecky, listen to me. Today Charlotte's going to have lots of presents and tomorrow she won't remember who's given her what. What she might remember is that you came to her party and you were a lot of fun.'

My Mother came to a decision.

'I'm going to give you tuppence.'

'What sort of present can I get for tuppence?' I cried in despair.

'Listen to me,' my Mother said, 'Go down to old Stan at the allotments and tell him you want the biggest bunch of flowers you can get for tuppence.'

'Flowers?' I cried in horror, 'Flowers!'

'Believe you me,' Auntie Bella advised, 'Girls like flowers.'

'Go and see old Stan,' said my Mother, 'He won't disappoint you. He'll make you up a lovely bouquet. And you can change that jersey before you go.'

She grabbed me before I could resist and checked behind my ears for potato patches.

'You won't believe this, Bella,' she cried, 'But he's actually washed his face! It must be love!'

And so it was that I proceeded to Mr. MacAtominey's butcher shop, in my best jersey with knitted tie attached, armed with a huge bouquet of flowers from old Stan the Allotment Man and my heart beating like an great bass drum. When I entered his marble halls Mr. MacAtominey switched off his mincing machine and came forward, wiping his hands on his apron. He stopped short when he saw it was me.

'Not you again! I hardly recognised you with your hair combed.'

I admitted, 'I haven't come to buy anything.'

'I didn't think so,' admitted the amiable butcher, 'And I don't suppose the flowers are for me, are they?'

I apologised without reserve.

'No, I'm sorry. You see, Mr. MacAtominey, I don't have a present, but Our Mam said.'

Mr. MacAtominey smiled on me.

'Go through, son,' he said, 'You're just in time for tea.'

His amiability even extended to the kindly man going to open the house door to usher me into the party. The noise of excited children, laughing and talking, the hubbub of a happy birthday flooded the shop. At that point my heart stopped. I lost my nerve. I stood paralysed with fear.

'Go on through, son,' repeated Mr. MacAtominey, 'I'm sure Charlotte will be pleased to see you.'

From a dry throat I heard me say, 'I can't stop. I've got to see somebody in hospital.'

'I'm very sorry to hear that.'

He closed the house door and the party vanished.

I said, desperately, 'They're very, very ill. If I don't go now they'll be dead before I get there.'

The butcher cried, 'Great steaming puddens!'

I offered Old Stan's generous bouquet.

'Could you give the flowers to Charlotte and say, Happy Birthday for me?'

I was beginning to believe the story of the dying relatives all lying in a row in a hospital ward, pale faces turned towards the door for a last glimpse of their beloved son, grandson, nephew before they drew a last lingering breath and departed this vale of tears.

Mr. MacAtominey, grave of eye, said, 'No bother, son. But you're going to miss a grand tea. There's three different jellies and ice cream.'

'Three different jellies?' I repeated wistfully, 'And ice cream?'

'Lemon, raspberry and strawberry, I understand,' recited the kindly butcher, persuasively, 'Why not go on through and give the flowers to Charlotte yourself?'

He opened the house door and again the melodious music of happy children filled the shop. But cowardice overpowered me.

'I have to go, Mr. MacAtominey.'

The butcher, face glowing like the moon over the flowery bank where the wild thyme grew, tried yet again, 'I know she'll love them. Charlie's never had a bouquet before. Stay just a moment, eh? And I'll fetch her out?'

The ward-long line of beds assailed me, grey faces, failing arms reaching out for just one last word, one final embrace.

I cried, 'They're breathing their last. They'll give a last lingering sigh and I don't want to miss that.'

As I left the shop Mrs. MacAtominey cried, 'Hang on, son! What's your name?'

To himself as the door closed he said, 'There's one rum little beggar.'

Once out in Albert Road, I leant against a wall. I couldn't breathe. I couldn't walk or run. I couldn't cry or laugh. I had this great pain in my chest and I knew it would never leave me. I only wished to die. Then a voice spoke to me.

'Lecky?'

'Oh, Uncle Freddie!' I cried.

'You look a bit rough, old sausage,' said my Uncle, 'That tom cat's not been dragging you about again, has he?'

I lamented, 'I've missed you so much! Where've you been?'

'I've been walking with giants, old son, that's where I've been, walking with giants.'

'No, you haven't. There's been photographs in the papers and Auntie Bella's been trying not to believe it was you. I knew it was you. But I'm supposed to lay off you for the Scholarship. So I didn't say anything.'

'It's been a momentous week,' Uncle Freddie said soberly.

'It's been an awful week. Something terrible has happened to me.'

'What's happened, old sausage?'

I hesitated to tell him.

'Whatever it is you can tell me.'

'I've fallen in love with Charlotte MacAtominey.'

Surprised, he cried, 'Not the butcher's daughter?'

'Her Granny's black puddens were famous from Billingham to Berwick,' I reminded him.

'Then why do you look like a wet weekend?'

I cried, 'The coble's turned over and thrown me into the raging sea.'

'Then swim for the shore, old son!' he urged me, gripping me by the shoulder, 'Strike out for very life!'

'But Charlotte's shouting for Norman Richardson. Not me. He got the personal invitation to her party.'

I was near to tears.

'I'm drowning, Uncle Freddie. Help me. I'm drowning.'

Uncle Freddie held me in his arms in Albert Road and nobody passing seemed to notice.

'Shush, old sausage, shush. Never mind. If it's any consolation, we all go through this.'

'It hurts, Uncle Freddie,' I wept.

He wiped away my tears.

'I know it hurts,' he explained, 'It hurts like Hereford. But it won't hurt forever and tomorrow's another day.'

'And you weren't here,' I complained.

'I'm sorry,' he said, 'I was looking the other way. All of which makes my news small beer.'

'What news?'

'I've spent my time with the Prince, showing him how hard life is on Tyneside. Telling him what needs to be done to put the country back on its feet. And David agrees with me.'

'And Edward as well?' I asked. The day looked less grey in the presence of my Uncle.

'His full name,' Uncle Freddie announced, 'is Edward Albert Christian George Andrew Patrick David.'

'They have everything,' I commented, 'Even more names than we do.'

'But I hope,' he predicted, 'for the first time ever we'll have a King who is prepared to roll up his sleeves and set to work to change things. If the world won't move, then we will move it. So take heart, old sausage. The sun will shine again and there'll be other lasses.'

I shook my head sombrely.

'Not for me,' I declared, 'When I die you'll find Charlotte MacAtominey engraved on my heart.'

Uncle Freddie laughed out loud. I regarded him soberly.

'I always said you were a bighearted bairn,' he explained, 'Sorry, but I couldn't resist the joke, old sausage.'

To my surprise I found myself smiling.

'That's the ticket,' my Uncle encouraged me, 'What's the use of worrying? It never was worthwhile. Look, I'm away for fish teas. David's in the kitchen. Keep him company.'

Marching away he called, 'You'll feel like your old self when you've wrapped yourself round a haddock and chips.'

'Don't go to Simpson's, Uncle Freddie,' I cried.

I knew The Heir To The Throne was in Auntie Bella's kitchen even before I opened the scullery door. The scent of Turkish tobacco had curled under the door into the yard and was not yet subdued by the perfume of Carbolic soap, the parfum naturel of Hurworth Place.

Our chum David was relaxing in Auntie Bella's chair, dressed it seemed to me as an Admiral in the Swiss Navy or the Commissionaire at the Kino.

'Wha'd'you think, Lackey, old sport?' he chirruped, 'Yachting togs, eh?

Can't toodle about on a boat thing without looking the part. Though to be honest, Lackey, I actually couldn't tell you which is port or starboard. Used to be a frightful nuisance on the old HINDUSTAN when I was a middie. Always bumping into hard things when I was officer of the watch. Even when I got it right the helmsman would steer the boat in the opposite direction to what I said because I normally got it wrong anyway.'

He paused and said, 'I say, old chap, you're looking positively gloomy.'

'It's nothing.'

The Heir To The Throne contradicted me.

'Yes, it is. I can see by your face you've been blubbing. Pretty serious by the look of you! The least a chap can do is listen to another chap's tale of woe.'

I said, 'I've found out.'

The Prince leaned forward sympathetically.

'What've you found out, old thing?'

'Love isn't what I thought it was. It hurts in my stomach and in my chest. I thought it was meant to make you happy.'

Our chum David said, thoughtfully, 'Sometimes it does and sometimes it doesn't.'

'And it gets so big it blots out everything else. Everything else I cared about has become very small. Nothing matters. Not even the Grammar School,' I explained.

Edward Albert Christian George Andrew Patrick David said, 'Nothing matters except the person you love.'

We looked at one another in complete agreement, prince and pauper.

'And I want to be with her,' I said.

'And you can't be,' sighed the Prince.

'She doesn't want me,' I lamented, 'Is it always like this? Isn't Amor supposed to wink at Omnia?'

The Prince drew upon his aromatic cigarette for comfort.

'We have it on the very best authority. True love overcomes all obstacles. When you find your true love, I assure you, it will be wonderful, old chap.'

He rose from Auntie Bella's chair and stubbed out his cigarette on her spotlessly blackleaded grate.

I said, 'I don't want to be in love.'

'Sorry, old thing,' said The Heir To The Throne, 'We have no choice in the matter. Love is the master of princes and paupers.'

With these words, our chum David shook me by the hand, said, 'Been a pleasure to make your acquaintance, old sport' and exited Auntie Bella's kitchen. All that remained of royalty was the faint aroma of Turkish tobacco.

When Uncle Freddie finally returned from Simpson's chip shop via the police station, having had a fight with Wally Simpson, and getting his photograph in the Chronicle yet again: TATTOO ARTISTE GETS BATTERING IN CHIPSHOP AFTER CUSTOMER GETS THE NEEDLE, the Prince had long gone. Never to be seen in Jarrow again.

You know the rest of the story. Or most of it. The young King declares his love for Mrs. Simpson. Constitutional crisis. Dramatic meetings in Downing Street. But perhaps you didn't know it was all my fault that King Edward decided to abdicate. Blame hapless Lecky falling in love with Charlotte MacAtominey, hair as red as fire and eyes as green as the sea. Blame love itself, that wilful tyrant to whom we're all enslaved.

Once I had a dream and in that dream, above the watery pasture of the harbour, above Knott's Flats, stretching to Collingwood's column where the Trafalgar cannon stand mute and dreadful, I read the words, emblazoned upon the sky, HEART'S ACHE, HEART'S EASE. And in this dream my beloved Uncle Freddie and I were sitting off the Tyne piers, in a shabby coble borrowed from Elijah Lawes, with a bag full of mackerel at our feet, waiting for the tide to turn, to scull back up-river to the Satellite quay. In this dream I asked Uncle Freddie what the words meant and he answered me by saying, 'True stories have a habit of turning out very awkward sometimes, old sausage.'

Eleven

UNCLE FREDDIE AND I WERE AMBLING down Ferry Street discussing the difference between a raven and a writing desk when we saw Death's Door walking his mare Queenie and cart up the road towards us.

I knew, as Uncle Freddie had once told me, you could judge a man by whether he walked his horse up a bank or added to its burden, but Death's Door was not a popular figure in Jarrow. He was taller than most men with an unsmiling face, wore a battered bowler with a white feather in the band and ignored everybody. He and Uncle Freddie would exchange polite nods, but Death's Door wasn't the sort who would discuss the difference between a raven and a writing desk.

Death's Door and the cart loaded with somebody's scraps of furniture were almost abreast of us when something totally unexpected happened.

Queenie stopped, shook her head and her legs shot out sideways and she fell, dragging Death's Door down with her. The fall pulled the cart from its offside wheels and Uncle Freddie ran forward to pull the cart back from toppling over. I stood frozen and Uncle Freddie swung a heavy box from the cart to jam behind the back wheel of the cart.

Death's Door was on his knees stroking the old mare's head.

'Is she dying?' I asked, shocked by the speed of tragedy. Uncle Freddie nodded.

The mare's bladder opened and her water ran into the gutter and down the road. I could hear the urine ringing in the dry drain.

Death's Door began to loosen buckles and ease the bit from Queenie's mouth. Then I saw a second unexpected thing. The man was crying, the tears running unchecked down his cheeks. I looked at Uncle Freddie in astonishment. He turned to three lads who'd stopped to watch.

'D'y'know Billy Knacker's yard?' my Uncle asked.

They nodded, scarcely able to take their eyes off the dead horse.

'Then run to Billy's and tell him there's a job here for him,' he ordered, 'He'll mebbes have a penny for yi.'

The boys ran for the knacker's yard and Uncle Freddie joined Death's Door in stripping the harness from the old mare. They worked together without saying a word to one another. When the task was completed both men rose to their feet.

'Billy'll be here any time now,' Uncle Freddie said.

Death's Door nodded.

Uncle Freddie said, 'We'll leave you to it then, Ernie.'

Death's Door nodded again and we walked away.

As we walked I said, 'He was crying.'

Uncle Freddie said nothing.

'I never would have expected him to cry.' I explained.

Uncle Freddie said nothing.

'Not over a horse,' I added.

Uncle Freddie stopped and looked at me.

'You wouldn't think a man might cry at the death of an old friend? Perhaps his only friend?'

'But not Death's Door,' I retorted, 'He's not like that.'

'Not like what?'

I had no answer.

'You mean not like us? Not like you?' he demanded, 'Love has many faces. The man loved that faithful mare. They shared everything together, wind and rain, hail and snow. And sunshine if it ever shines in Jarrow. When Queenie died he wept. Like any man with an ounce of decent feeling would do.'

When we turned into the bottom road there was Ali Jamjar sitting on his cart reading an old newspaper while Bucephalus enjoyed the contents of his nosebag.

'Ali!' cried my Uncle, 'A sight for sore eyes!'

Ali lowered his newspaper and Bucephalus raised his long nose.

'Freddie, old friend!' cried Ali Jamjar, 'What can I avoid doing for you today?'

'Oh, Mister Jamjar,' I cried, 'Death's Door's horse is dead in Ferry Street,'

'With a load of furniture,' suggested my Uncle Freddie.

Ali said, 'So you want Ali to go and help him out?'

'You've nothing much on your cart,' I assured him.

'Only,' said Ali, 'Because Jarrow folk is so poor now they's wearing all the rags and boiling up the bones for broth.'

'You could give the man a hand?' suggested my Uncle.

'He was crying,' I said rashly.

Ali looked at Uncle Freddie and my Uncle shrugged. Ali folded up his newspaper and my Uncle removed Bucephalus's nosebag.

'Only if the man don't talk, talk, talk to me all the time,' said Ali and departed, 'One thing I cannot stand no way is a chatterbox.'

As we crossed the barren ground to the Jarrow-Howdon ferry Uncle Freddie said to me, 'Let me tell you something about that man.'

'Death's Door?'

'His real name,' my Uncle replied, ' is Ernest Butcher. He was a sergeant in the East Lancs when they were shipped to Gallipoli. Have you heard of Gallipoli?'

'Yes. They were going to march on Constantinople, but they didn't.'

'Thousands of lads, British, French, Anzacs died hanging on to that cliff edge and a scraping of land for eight months. Ernie Butcher was one of the lucky ones. He came home with two machine gun bullets in his chest. One too close to his heart to be moved. He was honourably discharged to die, but he didn't.'

'I'm glad he didn't,' I agreed.

'Then one day a lady gave him a white feather because he wasn't in uniform serving King and Country.'

I stopped and Uncle Freddie stopped as if tied to me. The ferry nosed into the landing and I could hear the rattle of the chains as the ramp went down.

I said, 'And he wears the white feather in his dut.'

'Mebbes the worst wounds are not delivered on the battlefield,' suggested my Uncle.

'I shall never call him Death's Door again, ' I vowed.

When I was a skinny bairn in Jarrow, I owned the ferry and spent many happy afternoons sailing backwards and forwards across the canny, coaly Tyne from Jarrow to Howdon and back. It was no concern of mine that it was a free ferry offering the opportunity to the unemployed on both banks of the Tyne to fruitlessly chase unavailable employment on either bank.

On that quiet afternoon with the river half-asleep, unemployed tugs dozing at their moorings and nothing bigger than a salle marie moving, even the gulls seemed half-hearted in their raucous squabbling overhead. We were the last of half a dozen passengers aboard, walking the restless ramp into the old Montrose where Uncle Freddie raised a hand to Captain Jack up at the wheelhouse door and Big Jack, the deckie, scrubbed my head in welcome before he started the chains reluctantly to withdraw the ramp. There were three men in the crew of the ferry, Captain Jack, a fierce pipe smoker, Big Billie, an amiable giant, and the dark mysterious presence only half-glimpsed below an open engineroom hatch Captain Jack referred to as That Yin, the engineer, as in 'if That Yin could get his heed out of his comic mebbes we could get across to Howdon afore teatime.'

Once aboard, the throbbing of the engine, the scent of hot oil, the music of the water held me as ever in its thrall. I knew, one day, if not today, Captain Jack would tire of his endless trudging to and fro and turn the Montrose's nose downriver for the open water and high adventure in the southern seas. I knew from the way the Captain bit down on his pipe, the way his hands hesitated on the wheel before he made his approach to the Howdon quay, the way his eyes lingered on seabound vessels that it was only touch and go whether the frustrated mariner would break his hateful bonds, spin the wheel and follow the tide for Pernambuco. When the day came that he made his break for freedom I wanted to be with him in the wheelhouse, ready to feed him bully beef sandwiches and tin mugs of grog as we battled to force the passage of the Horn in midwinter.

That afternoon we sat outside the wheelhouse, Uncle Freddie and me, high above the common herd, from whence we surveyed the crowded river, so many sleeping ships, so silent the shore. Together we watched the Jarrow shoreline, the wreckage of Palmer's recede as the ferry turned for Howdon and the silent yards of the north side.

My Uncle Freddie said, 'It's got to stop, old sausage.'

'What's got to stop?'

'Me filling your head with nonsense.'

I protested, 'It's not nonsense.'

'Your Mam's been on at me,' he reported reluctantly.

'Our Mam's always on about something.'

He said, 'The upshot of it all is you have to bring your mind to bear on the Scholarship.'

'I can do long multiplication,' I protested, 'I never forget to put the nought in now.'

My Uncle was silent for a moment and then he said, 'I left school when I was twelve and took on at Palmer's with the promise of an apprenticeship, cap cocked over me eye and a Woodbine behind me ear. Oh, I thought myself quite the fancy dan.'

I laughed at this image of my Uncle.

'But I wasn't,' he said sombrely, 'I was only a prisoner transferred between prisons.'

He looked at me and I wasn't laughing.

'Sorry,' I said.

'Nothing to be sorry for,' he said, 'And now the governor's turfed me out. I'm neither decus nor tutamen to anybody.'

When I queried his Latin, he explained, 'Neither use nor ornament.'

'You are to me, ' I declared stoutly and he smiled.

'Come the day you've got the vellum in your sweaty mitt you'll be glad I'm not there to embarrass you.'

'Never! I shall want you there! You have to be there!'

'So, as your Mam says, we must calm down the daftness.'

Did calm down the daftness include the goddess Charlotte

MacAtominey? For I had fallen helplessly in love with Charlotte MacAtominey, the butcher's daughter, hair as red as fire and eyes as green as the sea. It was, indeed, a time of great affliction and getting ever deeper. I was considering posing the question to Uncle Freddie as the ferry approached the Howdon quay and rubbed her grizzled flank against the landing. The ferry bell sounded, the engine reversed and idled and Big Billie released the chains that held the ramp. Down rattled the ramp and then followed our passengers safely landed. I was about to warn Uncle Freddie that I was to pose a most serious question to him that bore upon the calming of the daftness when two passengers ascended the ramp and entered the Montrose.

'Oh, no!' I cried, 'Charlotte MacAtominey's getting on. And Norman Richardson. What am I going to do?'

The searing humiliation of my failure to attend Charlotte's party was vivid in my mind. I writhed before Charlotte's sneering glance as she trampled Old Stan's flowers into the carpet watched by a gleeful Norman Richardson whose spiteful giggles blistered my brain. I saw all the laughing faces at the party pulling off the flower heads and Charlotte picking off the petals of Stan's prize roses. If Death is so merciful, then why did I not fall lifeless to the antique planking of the ferry, and with my last breath to my dear Uncle, kneeling on said planking pockmarked with discarded chewing gum, whisper, 'Tell Charlotte I forgive her. And she can have my cigarette cards.' Then depart this mortal coil with a lingering smile. I could almost hear Mrs. Richardson sigh, 'Whatever you say, that lad made a beautiful corpse.'

In the anguish of the soul I repeated my cry, 'What am I going to do?'

'Go down and say hello?' Uncle Freddie suggested.

'I can't,' I whimpered.

'Yes, you can,' Uncle Freddie said sternly, 'The little lass and Norman are going up to the bow. Go on!'

'I wouldn't know what to say,' I excused myself.

'Start with "Hello Charlotte",' Uncle Freddie suggested.

My mouth was dry as Shields sands at low tide.

Uncle Freddie addressed a passing gull, 'D'y'think his Mam's raised a coward?'

The herring gull considered the question, emptied his bowels and flew away to spread the scandal. I stood up and walked to the companionway. I felt sick and my legs wobbled. The ferry bell rang. Big Billie began to raise the ramp; the engine pulse quickened and the Montrose began to nudge away from the Howdon landing. I climbed down the companionway onto the deck.

Norman Richardson and Charlotte were sitting in the bow together. Norman was offering Charlotte a paper bag from which to choose a sweet. Charlotte was smiling and Norman's pudgy face was even smugger than usual. His Mammy's Boy quiff was glistening with Brylcreme. His other arm lay casually on the bulwark almost embracing Charlotte's shoulder while his fat knees were too close to Charlotte. At that moment I loathed Norman even as I adored Charlotte, her hair red as fire burning in the breeze and eyes as green as the sea that swept away any last ounce of commonsense I might have possessed. I utterly adored this paragon of beauty. If Charlotte MacAtominey had asked me to jump overboard I would've done so without a second thought.

I approached the happy couple sick in every sinew. I struggled to restrain myself from leaping upon obnoxious Norman, tearing off his ugly head and kicking it into the river. I would've rejoiced to watch him running round the deck like a headless chicken until I would take him by the arm he had nearly dared to place upon Charlotte and heave him into the river to look for his head.

Norman said, 'Well, look who it isn't! Wha'd'you want, Lecky Fergie?'

I said, 'Nothing from you. Hello, Charlotte!'

My goddess smiled at me. In my heart the sun shone and blue birds sang.

Charlotte said, 'Hello, Lecky. I didn't know you were on the ferry?'

I said, from a dry throat, 'I was up top. Helping the captain. I saw you get on.'

Norman Richardson sniggered. A momentary irritation crossed Charlotte's face.

I said, 'I just thought I'd come and say hello.'

Charlotte smiled at me and said, 'I'm glad you did.'

'Really?' I choked, head swimming.

'Don't talk to him, Charlotte,' said Norman crossly, waving the bag of sweets at her again. Charlotte ignored the paper bag and asked, 'Why shouldn't I talk to him?'

Norman was stumped, but only momentarily.

'He wipes his nose on his sleeve, that's why!'

I retorted indignantly, 'I do not!'

'And they don't have lavatory paper!'

Charlotte laughed and asked, 'It was you, wasn't it, who brought the bouquet to my party?'

I nodded miserably.

'Wrapped in newspaper!' rejoiced Norman Richardson.

Charlotte looked scorn on Norman.

'I never had a bouquet before. The flowers were beautiful. My mother put them in a vase and placed it in the centre of the table. She said it set the whole table off a treat. Thank you, Lecky! But I wish you'd come into the party.'

'I had to go to the hospital,' I lied, 'My Auntie and Uncle Arbuckle of Harbottle Street were very ill and they wanted a last look at me.'

'Are they alright now?' Charlotte asked.

'They're dead,' I said, 'But they got a last look and gave a long sigh and died.'

'I'm sorry,' said Charlotte and Norman snorted.

'Don't be,' I said, 'They'd been expecting it. They'd been married forty years and that was more than enough and everything was paid up so they were quite glad to go when their time came.'

'Huh!' said Norman, 'That's all I'm going to say. Huh!'

'You've said it twice,' I pointed out.

'Well, you can buzz off now,' Norman countered, 'Your time's up!'

'Shut up, Norman!' Charlotte ordered, 'Or I won't go skating with you.'

Charlotte smiled upon me and my head rang with the Hallelujah Chorus. In the summer of that smile all commonsense deserted me.

'I'll have to get back to help the captain, ' I said, 'But I was going to ask you to my party.'

'Party?' cried Norman my tormentor, 'He never has parties!'

Charlotte's smile embraced my very soul.

'Oh, Lecky, I'd love to come!' my darling cried.

'Don't listen to him, Charlotte,' Norman begged, 'He's telling lies! He's always telling lies! Everything he says is a lie!'

Even on the brink of the abyss when I might have scrambled to safety from the sliding scree I chose instead to jump into the gaping void.

'I'm not telling lies!' I cried, regardless of the consequences, 'I'm going to have a very big party! We're going to have four different jellies!'

'Four!' gasped Charlotte.

'Liar!' Norman cried jubilantly.

'And balloons! Lots of them!' I countered.

'Not in Hurworth Place, you're not!' cried Norman.

'And a cake?' Charlotte enquired.

'Our Dad's making the cake.'

Charlotte clapped her hands in pleasure.

'Oh, lovely!' she cried, ecstatic.

To add to her happiness I couldn't resist adding, 'And a conjuror!'

Norman was jubilant.

'I know he's telling lies, Charlotte! No conjuror would ever go near Hurworth Place!'

But nothing could stop my bolting horse now. I had lost both reins and stirrups.

'He's called Magnus the Magnificent! He's performed before all the crowned heads of Europe before they were executed! And he makes people disappear. I wish he'd make you disappear, Norman Richardson.'

'I'd love to come,' said Charlotte.

'You would?'

'Yes! When is the party?'

I hesitated to commit myself, but the situation was far beyond retrieval. I was clinging to the horse's neck as he bolted across treacherous ground, reins flapping and stirrups rapping the horse's sweating flanks.

'A week on Saturday. At four.'

Charlotte smiled and my very being melted with delight.

'Then I'll be there.'

'You'll be the guest of honour,' I assured her.

'Will I really?'

'Yes. You'll be treated like a princess.'

We became aware of Norman's presence.

'Huh! That's all I'm going to say! Huh!' sneered Norman Richardson, 'That's all I'm going to say!'

The ferry hooted, awakening me from a summer's dream.

'I'll have to go and help the captain now,' I said, 'Bye, Charlotte!'

'Bye, Lecky,' she said, 'Until a week on Saturday.'

From the companionway I watched them disembark. Charlotte waved to me and I waved back. Norman ignored me. As I climbed the steps to the wheelhouse, a colder breeze from the river caught me.

'Oh, grief! What have I done?' I cried, 'Something happened and my mouth ran away while my brain said stop!' But it wasn't true. A force greater than gravity had led me to destruction.

Twelve

UNCLE FREDDIE CRIED, 'YOU DID WHAT, YOU RHUBARB?'

The herring gulls echoed his disbelief, soaring above us, squawking, *He did what, he did what, he did what?*

'I invited Charlotte MacAtominey to my party,' I repeated miserably.

The squawking of the gulls above our heads rose to a disbelieving crescendo.

'What party is this?' asked Uncle Freddie.

'The party I'm not going to have a week on Saturday,' I answered. For a moment the gulls were silent and then they fell about the sky laughing their beaks off.

We sat in silence watching the unceasing tide.

Uncle Freddie said, 'What on earth possessed you, old sausage?'

I hesitated and then admitted, 'It all rushed out. I couldn't stop myself. Four different jellies. Balloons. A cake. And a conjuror.'

'A conjuror?' Uncle Freddie repeated, 'Where'd that come from?'

'In TWO BOYS, TWO WORLDS, the Honourable Arnold Spenser has a conjuror perform at his tenth birthday party at Ballyghillie House.'

'From a story book,' said Uncle Freddie sadly, shaking his head, 'You took it from a story book?'

I said, 'Magnus the Magnificent gives a wonderful performance.

In the finale he makes the pampered Honourable Arnold disappear, changing places with the ploughman's son, worthy Arthur Spencer who gives a party for all the village children. Only the Honourable Arnold can't come because he gets ploughman's palsy and dies.'

Uncle Freddie said, 'Lucky Arnold! There's not much ploughman's palsy in Jarrow.'

I felt the icy waters of despair beginning to close about my ankles and climb my legs with clammy fingers.

'What am I going to do?' I cried.

'How about,' suggested my Uncle, 'a berth as a cabin boy, sailing for South America to collect bananas?'

'I'll sail tomorrow!' I cried.

Uncle Freddie shook his head.

'Sadly, old sausage, the market for cabin boys has completely dried up since they got the electric trouser presses.'

'Then I'm doomed, Uncle Freddie, doomed, deadly doomed,' I mourned.

If I am ever to be re-united with my Mother in that place where there is no pain and suffering, no loss and no betrayal, where only love is, I will be standing on a staircase which will look much like Hurworth Place only the light through the landing window will shine eternally and I shall be listening, not to the singing of angels, but to the rattle of an old sewing machine, chuckle, chuckle. When I open the door at the head of the stairs I will find my Mother sitting at her sewing machine, head bent to the needle, chuckle, chuckle, oblivious to everything except a straight seam. Then she will look up, bite off the cotton and smile at me.

My Mother said, 'I thought you'd been lost at sea.'

'They don't want cabin boys any more,' I said, 'They've got the electric now.'

'I won't even ask what that means,' she said and bent again to her sewing. Chuckle, chuckle went the treadle. I sat on the arm of the Best Chair and watched her. Chuckle, chuckle, chuck went the treadle and stopped.

'I have this terrible feeling,' my Mother said, 'that you're going to announce the end of the world.'

'No, I'm not, Our Mam.'

'Good!' she replied, 'Because I cannot get on with you sitting there working yourself up to say something. It's been such a lovely, peaceful day. You're not going to say something to spoil it, are you?'

I admitted, 'I was going to ask you something.'

'The answer's no,' she replied promptly.

'How do you know what I'm going to ask?'

My Mother looked up at me with just the taste of a smile about her mouth.

'If it was something sensible,' she assured me, 'you wouldn't warn me in advance.'

'Then I won't ask.'

'Good,' said she, 'Then I won't refuse.'

The sewing machine began again, chuckle, chuckle, as she bent to her work. My mother's hands were never still. I see her now, head cocked, one thin hand patting the wheel, chuckle, chuckle, the other guiding the fabric, and wonder how she could be so content who had so little. The sewing machine stopped.

'I give in,' my mother said, 'I'm trying to do a tricky bit of sewing here while I'm waiting for you to go off bang. Best you go off bang afore I make a muck of this. Go on, pull the pin!'

I hesitated and then announced, 'I was going to ask you, please, if I could have a party, Our Mam?'

She sat silent for a moment, considering my request.

'Well, I suppose it could be worse. I was beginning to think you'd declared war on Germany.'

'Am I allowed to do that?'

'Yi've just been to a party. Isn't that enough?'

My Mother was unaware of my failure of nerve to cross the threshold to Charlotte MacAtominey's party. I'd waited across the road until the party ended before going home to lie about what a wonderful time I'd had and went to bed hungry. My Mother was a little peeved that the McConnell girls had come home with balloons and slices of cake whereas I had nothing.

'So much for tuppence spent on flowers for that lass,' she complained, 'I'm beginning to think twice about your Miss Macaroni.'

I rushed to defend Charlotte and defame myself.

'I ate the cake on the way home and the balloon burst,' I lied.

'So they skimped on the tea, did they?' she countered, 'The man's pockets are busting with money, but he skimps on his daughter's tea party!'

'There was masses for tea, Our Mam, honest!' I protested, scrambling for safe ground as the earth moved beneath my feet alarmingly, 'And Mrs. MacAtominey put our flowers in the middle of everything. She said it really set off the table.'

My Mother sniffed, partially mollified by this floral social success.

'But you ate the cake?' she countered, 'Your Dad would've liked to have seen that cake.'

I put on a penitent face.

'I didn't eat it,' I admitted, 'I dropped it.'

'Aha!' cried my Mother who had missed her vocation as a police interrogator, 'Now we're getting to the truth!'

Before she could frame the question, I offered, 'Before I could pick it up a dog ran off with it.'

'Whose dog? Did you see whose dog it was?'

'I don't know whose dog,' I answered, 'Just a big black dog,' and as inspiration offered, 'That's when the balloon burst when I was running after the dog.'

She sat in silence for a moment.

'It was probably a shop bought cake, but it would've been nice to have had a balloon about the house,' she said wistfully.

'Yi've just been to a party. Isn't that enough?'

'This would be my party.'

'Why would you want a party? It's not your birthday.'

'D'y'have to have a reason?'

'Yi don't just have parties out of the blue.'

'Norman Richardson's always having parties at his house,' I protested.

My Mother said icily, 'Don't mention that name in this house, thank you very much.'

'Why not?'

She snorted briefly.

'I can just imagine what kind of parties.'

I hastened to reassure her.

'He has all kinds of parties. They even had a Going-Away Party when Uncle Ronnie fell off the High Level Bridge.'

My Mother seemed impressed by this macabre gaiety.

'They never did!'

I began to feel I was making progress in my quest for a spectacular party that would leave Charlotte MacAtominey gazing at me with deathless adoration.

'It didn't start out like that,' I counselled, 'Mrs. Richardson was quite upset. She was just having an extra glass of port to strengthen her nerves when this man came. Mrs. Richardson thought he'd come for Uncle Ronnie's bits and pieces, but she'd already placed his watch and tiepin with Mister Goldman for safekeeping. For which she apologised profusely, but the man said that wasn't a problem and yes, he'd have a glass of port seeing as it was offered. Then the man said he was from the Insurance and that Mrs. Richardson's name was on the policy. She cheered up straightaway and sang a song and kicked her height.'

My Mother said sharply, 'I trust you weren't looking.'

'I saw a lot of elastic,' I admitted.

'The woman has no shame,' my Mother pronounced.

'That's how the Going Away Party for Uncle Ronnie started,' I concluded, 'Norman got Uncle Ronnie's silver-backed hair brushes and a thing for getting blackheads out. The Insurance man stayed for the party, but I had to come home. Missing all the fun.'

I was hoping my Mother would immediately realise that being deprived of the Going Away Party for Uncle Ronnie I should be compensated by having my own party. I gave her my Sad Child smile which sometimes may be mistaken for my I Forgive You smile.

She said, icily, 'Missing all what fun?'

'Norman said the Insurance man came headfirst down the banister and hit his head on the wooden pineapple at the bottom. Mrs. Richardson put him to bed and he stayed three days.'

My Mother seemed less than impressed.

'Mrs. Richardson says she has an open house policy. What's our policy, Our Mam?'

'Honesty's the best policy for the likes of us,' she replied.

'What about rich people?' I enquired.

My Mother snorted and said, 'You can't be rich and honest.'

We sat in silence for a moment, my Mother looking over her sewing and me, perched on the Best Chair, praying for an affirmative answer to the Question of the Moment. Finally I could bear the suspense no longer.

'Can I have a party, Our Mam? Please?'

My Mother began to sew, chuckle, chuckle, bending all her attention on the garment she was repairing. I waited until time ceased and then I slid from the Best Chair and headed for the door. My disappointment must've moved her because the sewing machine stopped. Chuckle, chuck.

She said, 'What would you want at this party?'

'Four kinds of jelly, balloons and a conjuror.'

'Try Buckingham Palace. They might oblige.'

'We could do without the balloons.'

At this time coloured balloons were just beginning to appear at the most extravagant of parties.

'You can cross off the conjuror as well.'

Seeking a compromise, I offered eagerly, 'I could say he'd sent his profuse apologies, but he'd been taken ill with leprosy. And the doctor had forbidden him to do tricks in case his fingers fell off.'

'Leprosy being a very common affliction in Jarrow,' my Mother commented.

'I didn't know that,' I said, surprised and quickly, 'So can I have a party, Our Mam?'

She was silent for a moment and then said, gently, 'How can we have a party, son? We've nowhere decent like the MacAtomineys.'

I'd never ever felt our simple home – our shelter from the stormy blast – was lacking in any amenity. I looked round upon our neat and tidy Room.

'We could have it in here! The MacAtomineys is no different.'

'With your Dad sleeping? He'd go hairless,' she said, and I knew she was right. I could picture my Father bursting in on the party and annihilating any jollification.

Stung to inspiration, I cried, 'What about the wash house?'

'The wash house?'

'If we had the copper fire on and a candle? It'd be lovely!' I pleaded, 'Please. Let me have a party in the wash house, please!'

'You're not having a party in the wash house. Or anywhere else,' she determined, 'Besides there's the food.'

She turned back to her sewing machine.

'What if I could get all the food?' I persisted.

'Come here,' my Mother said.

'What for?' I answered, but obeyed her. I stood before her as restive as a rabbit in the rhubarb.

'Bend down.'

I obeyed and she took me by the ear and looked me in the eye.

'I want to sew a button on your lip. When you feel the urge to promise Charlotte Macaroni the moon, you can fasten it tight.'

She tugged me closer, but didn't sew a button on my lip; she kissed me on the cheek.

'No party,' she said with a finality I understood.

Thirteen

I WENT DOWNSTAIRS TO AUNTIE BELLA'S kitchen to seek solace. Auntie Bella was busily ironing. The kitchen smelt of warm fresh-ironed linen, a place of peace in a maelstrom of emotion. I sat down on the fender, the hot water boiler at my back, the coal fire at my ear and the flat irons circulating above my head from the fire to the ironing board and back. I unloaded my frustration on this tired woman.

'But I have to have a party, Auntie Bella,' I insisted.

'Nobody,' said Auntie Bella, changing flat irons, 'has to have anything. Most folk have nothing.'

Which silenced me most effectively.

'But what I'd like you to do,' she continued, 'is to finish off reading me THE FORGOTTEN PRINCESS. That would be better to me than a bottle of champagne!'

I don't suppose this sweet lady ever had a sip of champagne in her entire life. To have me reading to her compared favourably to a bottle of champagne was high praise. But how hard it is to learn that happiness is composed of such simplicities as a trivial story told one to another. When my heart aches I console my erratic organ with memories of Auntie Bella ironing, the rustle of coals, the scent of fresh linen, and me, reading a cheap romance aloud from the fender. Oh, Wilderness were Paradise enow!

'Go on, ' commanded my dear Aunt, 'from where Princess Alice is locked up in the castle dungeon for telling everybody her father, King Rudolf, has died.'

The sixpenny romance published by Chatter & Windows was at my elbow on the fender, bookmark in place. We never turned down the corner of a page. I began to read.

Chapter Nineteen. The icy silence of the cell was rudely broken as the key turned in the lock and the ironclad door was thrust open. Princess Alice rose trembling from her stool, shading her eyes against the lantern's glare. Into the circle of light strode the Court Chamberlain, Lord Malvain. 'Forgive the intrusion, your Highness,' the old courtier began.

I was already so wrapped in the story that when Auntie Bella returned an iron to the fire I was as startled as Princess Alice.

'Forgive the intrusion?' Auntie Bella snorted, 'When the poor lass's locked up in durance vile? She'd be glad of any company.'

I waited until she'd returned to the ironing board before I continued reading.

'Please state the purpose of your visit, sir,' replied Alice, 'Be quick. I have become reconciled to being solitary.'

'Your Highness,' said the Chamberlain, 'I seek the answer to a question that puzzles me greatly.' 'Ask your question', responded the Princess, 'And then leave me to the company of my thoughts.'

'Hold on half a tick, Lecky,' announced my Aunt, 'I'll have to pop down the yard. It's the excitement. I'll leave you to the company of your thoughts while I immure myself in dungeon deep.'

Auntie Bella vanished out of the kitchen door and I closed the book in my lap, keeping our place with a finger. We had a rule that if either of us felt the call of nature the other must not read on ahead. So I sat in silence and let the kitchen exercise its gentle magic upon me. Illuminated by the dying day, the fitful flames of a coal fire, this simple kitchen was the magic stage on which strutted a thousand characters from a hundred books, spouting their nonsense, entrancing delightfully the woman and the child. Who would exchange such a childhood for the regal richness of any royal court?

Auntie Bella came into the scullery where I heard her rinse her hands in the washing up bowl. When she came into the kitchen she took a spill from the tin on the mantelpiece and lit the gaslight. The gas lit with a plop and the mantle flared.

'And then, the lighting of the lamp,' I quoted. I said this every time she lit the gas. From where it came I could never remember, but it seemed appropriate as the mantle flared and the comforting bee buzz of the burning gas began.

'There we are. We'll have that kettle on now,' she said as if this were not our normal practice. She brought back with her a snap of cold air from the yard, a hint of carbolic soap, twilight in her hair and sat down on the fender to rub her ankles briskly. I see it all so clearly as I saw it long ago.

'Now what was Lord Malvain going to ask her?'

I opened the book and began to read.

The Court Chamberlain hesitated and then ventured, 'The Court is in turmoil. The country in ferment. Because of this terrible thing you have done. Why have you spread this rumour of the King's death?'

With satisfaction, Auntie Bella said, 'We're coming to the crust of it at last!'

We exchanged glances of expectation.

'My Lord Malvain,' answered the Princess, 'It was no fault of mine that my mother died giving birth to me.'

'Aha!' cried my peerless Aunt, 'A motherless child!'

Her exclamations were never an interruption of the text, but an enlivening commentary.

'Never since my first breath has his Majesty looked upon me with loving regard.'

'I thought it was something like that!' she commented.

I continued to unravel the mystery of the Princess's denial of her father.

'I have been a stranger to him all my life. I, who have never known a mother, have never shared a father's love. Now he is enchanted by this wicked woman I can bear it no longer. I have no father. My father is dead. I am an orphan child.'

'Oh, Lecky, how awful! Poor lamb!' my gentle Aunt cried.

'It was then the dark shape in the doorway took substance. King Rudolf himself entered the wretched dungeon to which he had confined his erring daughter.'

Auntie Bella said, 'He must've heard everything!'

Princess Alice drew back, trembling as much from terror as from cold. The King advanced, stretched out his arms, and cried, 'My daughter, oh, my daughter, how I have wronged thee! Come to my arms, my precious child! How can you ever forgive the waste of these lost years?' Princess Alice flew into her father's arms with a silent cry of joy.

Blinded by tears, I ceased to read. Auntie Bella and I hugged one another, tears tumbling freely to dampen the pages of THE FORGOTTEN PRINCESS. Then we blew our noses loudly, smiled bravely, mashed a pot of tea, burnt some bread and felt ever so much better.

Fourteen

ABOVE THE DOUBLE-FRONTED SHOP in regal scarlet and gold the fascia proclaimed *JOBLING FAMILY BUTCHER As Patronised by Sir Charles Mark Palmer, Baronet, First Mayor of Jarrow.*

Uncle Freddie had told me the truth of this fulsome gilding was that a man bearing some resemblance to Charles Palmer – a beard and a stern expression – had once bought a pork pie from the present Mr. Jobling's grandfather and shared it with his dog on the pavement. The dog, however, was the spitting image of Sir Charles's black Labrador.

I waited until the shop was empty before entering. Mr. Jobling came briskly into the shop and smiled on seeing me. I responded with my Sad Child's smile.

Mr. Jobling beamed upon me.

'Before you say a word, young man. How's your Mother keeping? All well, I trust?'

'In the pink,' I answered, 'Bit of a cough. But nothing too phlegmy.'

Mr. Jobling, the kindest of men, had a secret affection for my Mother that displayed itself in tuppence off the shilling and gifts of sweetbreads and other fleshly delicacies. Shamelessly I made best use of this affection.

The amiable butcher went on to say, 'I saw her at St. Thomas's picnic, but, of course, I didn't speak. She was having such a jolly time, running the races for the lasses! I hope I didn't embarrass her, being the only gentleman watching the lasses running?'

'Not at all,' I responded, 'In fact, she said to me, do you know Mr. Jobling was the only gentleman who bothered to watch the lasses run which was much appreciated. I shall have to consider next year whether he might like to present the prizes to the winners.'

Mr. Jobling struggled to contain his emotions.

'Did your Mother really say that?' he stumbled, 'About being bothered. And presenting the prizes next year?'

'As sure as I'm standing here,' I lied.

'It would be a great honour,' he answered humbly, 'A great honour. If your Mother mentioned it again, you might like to assure her that I'd be honoured, deeply honoured.'

'You may rely on me,' I assured him.

Mr. Jobling recollected that he was a butcher and I a potential customer.

'Well now, young Lochinvar, what can I do for you today?'

I gave him my Sad Child smile and said, 'I've come round to give you the bad news. We've got a bereavement.'

The kindly man's jaw fell like melting snow from our wash house roof.

'Our Dad's died.'

The butcher dropped his cleaver. It rang on the tiled floor like a funeral bell.

'Your father?'

'I'm nearly an orphan now.'

Mr. Jobling's honest face reflected true sympathy.

'Dear me! Oh, dear me! You poor lad!'

'I'm poorer than ever now.'

'Was it expected? Or was it sudden?' the good man asked.

'Quite sudden, ' I assured him, 'One minute he was alive and kicking and the next he was dead as a doorknob.'

A terrible thought struck Mr. Jobling.

'Oh, your poor mother! Is she bearing up?'

'She's bearing up all right, ' I reassured him, 'But we'll have to have men to carry the coffin when we bury him.'

Mr. Jobling pondered upon this sad news, shaking his head, quite close to tears.

'Although I have never met your late father,' he began, but I interrupted to chide him, saying, 'You mustn't speak ill of the dead. He was a very good timekeeper. He was never late.'

He looked at me, seemed about to say something and then asked, humbly, 'May I ask when the sad occasion is to be? To pay my respects like.'

'A week on Saturday,' I reported.

'Saturday week?' he responded, 'A week on Saturday? Are you sure?'

I said, 'Our Mam wants to keep him as long as possible. She says, when you're gone, you're gone. A lot of people want to have a last look at him. Uncle and Auntie Mackenzie are coming from Australia. They were transported, but they're letting them come back for Our Dad's funeral.'

Mr. Jobling nodded vaguely as if struggling for comprehension and asked, 'Have you refrigeration?'

'Only a bit of a cough,' I answered, 'Nothing infectious.'

I gave him my Sad Child smile again, and pronounced, 'When we get back from burying him in the ground we'll be very hungry. You have to dig a big hole. Our Mam was wondering whether you might have any sausages or saveloys or bits of ham or pigs' feet left over for the tea? After they've washed their hands, of course.'

Mr. Jobling was on safe ground here. Catering for wakes and funerals was something he understood.

He smiled upon me, his Sad Butcher's smile, and said, 'Don't you worry, lad. I'll see your mother has everything she needs in that line.'

'Thank you, Mr. Jobling,' I said, greatly relieved, 'I'll come round next week Saturday morning and collect it then, shall I?'

'God bless you, son!' said Mr. Jobling, in a tremulous voice, 'I should think your mother's very proud of her brave little lad, eh? A real comfort to her!'

'Some of those little pork pies would be very comforting,' I suggested.

The honest butcher blew his nose loudly on the corner of his apron, presented me with a saveloy, patted me on the head and regarded my departure fondly.

Fifteen

ANOTHER PLACE OF GREAT COMFORT to me, in times of deep affliction, was our washhouse. It was Our Mam and Auntie Bella's place of business, and sometime store for mangle, poss tub and poss stick, but to me it was a refuge from the stormy blast. At one end of the washhouse was the fireplace, above which was the great boiling copper, covered, when not in use, by a wooden lid. Even when the fire was dying, the copper kept its heat and to curl up on Hector's shield was sheer bliss.

I was sitting on the copper jiggling a knife blade in the back of the china pig trying to extract money from my moneybox when the door opened and Uncle Freddie came in.

'What are you doing, hiding away in here, old sausage?' he asked, 'Your Mam's asking for you.'

I shook the china pig at him in exasperation.

'I'm trying to get my money out of this pig,' I grumbled, 'All I'm getting is foreign coins. I'd be rich now if I was French.'

'Why would you be doing that?' asked my most percipient Uncle, 'That pig has been undisturbed for many moons.'

I stopped jiggling fruitlessly with the table knife to say, 'I'm going to have my party in here.'

Uncle Freddie came to lean against the copper, enjoying the warmth of the dying fire on his legs.

'I thought your Mam said no to a party?'

'I'm not going to bother her,' I answered.

With my tongue sticking out of my mouth like my Father about to sign some document, I struggled to keep the coin on the knife blade and withdraw it from the pig.

'If I can find tuppence I can get a bent loaf and broken cakes from the market on Friday night and mend them. Mr. Jobling's promised to give me—'

I got no further for my Uncle interrupted me to announce, 'Your Mam's said no.'

The coin rang dully on the wooden top of the copper.

'There!' I cried, 'A penny!'

'Are you listening to me?' Uncle Freddie asked.

'She meant in the house,' I answered, tongue protruding, eyes on the knife blade.

The coin fell from the pig. I picked it up only to exclaim in disgust, 'Another ten centimes. I don't know how there's any money left in France.'

Uncle Freddie persisted, 'I don't think you should go behind your Mam's back, old sausage.'

'Tell me the law that says you can't have a party in your own wash house. You can't, can you?' I declaimed, but I didn't meet his eye.

Another coin slid down the knife blade.

'A happ'nny!' I crowed, 'I told you there was real money in this pig.'

'This is not a good idea,' my Uncle declared.

I put down the pig and the knife. I was near to despair, my heart breaking, torn between tears and desperation.

'I must have a party, Uncle Freddie. Don't y'see? I just must have a party. If I didn't have a party for Charlotte I'd die.'

Then I began to cry which if I wasn't being honest I wouldn't admit.

'*He that can love, unloved, again, Hath better store of love than brain,*' he recited, 'And you, old sausage, have more than your share.'

He picked me up, slung me over his shoulder and carried me upstairs to my Mother. By the time we got to the top of the stairs we were both laughing.

On the landing I knew something was wrong. The bedroom door was open. My father was up and it wasn't his time. Uncle Freddie dropped me on the landing.

'One parcel delivered, Mary,' he called, winked at me and clattered down the stairs.

I was going to tiptoe past the kitchen door for the Room, but my Mother's voice stopped me in my tracks.

'Lecky!' she shouted, 'Get yourself in here!'

I opened the kitchen door and entered cautiously. My Father was sitting at the kitchen table. My Mother was standing at his elbow.

'Yes, Our Mam?' I said.

My Father was about to speak, but my Mother with a hand on his shoulder said, 'Let me handle this, Davie.'

My Father grumbled, 'What he needs is a touch of the belt.'

'I'll say what he needs,' my Mother insisted and to me she said, 'I've just had the strangest experience at my own front door.'

'Yes, Our Mam?'

Was it the old Sikh gentleman who went from door to door with his tray of trivialities? He had the habit of casting a handful of dried petals in blessing over whoever opened the door. Mr. Chamberlain had taken such an aversion to being hit in the face with dead flower bits that he chased the donor to the railway where his prey, being remarkably spry for his age, had vaulted the railway wall and escaped across the railway tracks. Mr. Chamberlain had thrown a stone in blessing that hit the old Sikh's turban, fortunately without dislodging it.

My Mother said, 'Lecky, I've just opened the front door to find Mr. Jobling standing on the step in his Sunday suit complete with black tie, black armband and what looks like the oldest bowler hat in Jarrow.'

My heart stopped. I wished I were dead.

'Oh, no!' I cried.

My Father, restrained from rising by my Mother shouted, 'I'll give you, oh, no, yi little bugger!'

'Davie!' my Mother reprimanded him, 'Language!'

With her right hand holding my Father firmly in his chair my Mother said, 'Mr. Jobling, twiddling with his bowler as if he was either going to take collection or play the tambourine, said to me, 'I was very sorry to hear your husband had passed away, Mrs. Ferguson. Please accept my condolences."

'Oh, no!' I cried again.

My Father again shouted, 'I'll give you, oh, no, yi little!' but refrained from swearing.

My Mother continued while my bladder filled to overflowing, saying, 'So I stood there like a stookie while he said, 'Mrs. Ferguson, you may rely on me for the funereal meats,' and, 'You're a lucky woman to have such a grand wee lad' and walked away.'

There was a silence in the kitchen like the end of days. A fly on the flypaper buzzed and my Mother asked, 'Would the grand wee lad care to explain why he told the butcher his father was dead?'

I hesitated to speak, my eyes being upon my Father who sat steaming like an overburdened boiler. I gestured at him, and said, dolefully, 'If I tell you he'll only hit me.'

'No, he won't,' my Mother said.

My Father's face expressed a contrariwise opinion.

'Yes, he will!'

'No, he won't!' my Mother repeated firmly, looking down upon my Father.

'Yes, he will! You can see the madness in his eyes!'

To me, she said, 'I said, he won't touch you,' and to my father, 'Davie, you've been warned!'

I stood on jelly legs in an unhappy silence until she said, 'Lecky, we're very upset, as you can imagine. But there must be some reason for saying such a terrible thing that made sense to you. Even if to nobody else.'

There was no anger in her voice. That made it all the harder to bear, but there was no escape.

'I wanted Mr. Jobling to give me things for my party.'

The kitchen table shook as my Father restrained himself from throwing it aside to reach me and trample my lifeless form into the linoleum.

'What bliddy party?' he roared.

My Mother silenced him with a glance.

'That was the funereal meats on offer, was it? And that's why you told him your father was dead? For a handful of sausage rolls?'

The words carried such contempt.

'No. It was all in THE FORGOTTEN PRINCESS.'

My Mother and Father exchanged glances of incomprehension.

'What was?' my Mother asked.

'Princess Alice was in the dungeon and the Chamberlain came in and asked her, 'Why have you spread this rumour of the King's death?''

My Father growled, 'This is Bella and her tuppenny romances again!'

'Go on, Lecky,' my Mother ordered.

'And the princess says, "It was no fault of mine that my mother died giving birth to me.""

'Well, at least you didn't have me pushing up the daisies,' said my Mother.

I assured her, 'I wouldn't do that.'

'Does any of this make any bliddy sense?' my Father shouted.

'And the princess says, "I have been a stranger to my father all my life. I, who have never known a mother, have never shared a father's love. I have no father. My father is dead. I am an orphan child.""

'Oh, Lecky!' my Mother cried.

'And then King Rudolf comes in and the Princess thinks he's going to hit her. But he doesn't,' I said hopefully, 'But instead the King begs her forgiveness and she flies to his arms with a silent cry of joy.'

As nobody was speaking to me upstairs and I wasn't allowed to go into Auntie Bella's kitchen I went to find comfort on Hector's shield above the cooling copper. There I resolved to spend the remainder of my days. I might even become renowned as the Hermit of Hurworth and in the years to come people might come from all over to visit the old graybeard in his cell and listen to his words of wisdom. It seemed an appealing career prospect.

The washhouse door opened and I tensed myself for a confrontation with my Father.

Uncle Freddie asked, 'Lecky! Are you in here?'

I heard him strike a match that flared into flame.

'Yes, Uncle Freddie.'

He came forward and applied the match to the stump of candle by the boiler. Then he went to the door and called, 'He's here, Bella.'

He closed the washhouse door and returned to me.

'What on earth are you doing here, old sausage?'

I moved over so he could hitch himself onto the copper.

'I've decided to become a hermit,' I told him.

'Won't you be lonely?'

'After a bit there'll be loads of people coming to ask advice of the hermit or just to peer in the washhouse at him,' I explained.

'Fair enough,' he said, 'Not everybody's cup of tea.'

'But I won't have to wash or anything,' I said, 'Hermits don't have to worry about dirt.'

'Well, you've certainly kicked up more dust than a herd of pit elephants, old sausage.'

'It's him!' I said, 'He swore he's going to throw all my books into the stoke hole at the bakery. D'y'think he will?'

'He won't,' Uncle Freddie assured me, 'Your Dad would never harm a book.'

'He was mad enough for murder,' I warned him, 'You should've seen his face. His eyes were popping out and his mouth was slathering to get at me!'

'What I don't understand is why you did it?'

'I thought he'd cry, "Oh, my son, how I have wronged you!"'

'But he didn't?'

I gave a sardonic laugh

'He stretched out his arms all right, but it wasn't forra hug. I never got the chance to give the silent cry of joy.'

My revered Uncle sat deep in thought for a moment and then suggested, 'The trouble is, old sausage, you and your Dad speak different languages.'

I defended myself.

'He said I was a doolie. I know what that means.'

'And you told him he didn't love you. Which d'y'think is worse?'

Before I could think of an answer the latch of the washhouse door lifted and an older man, ill-dressed, a stranger to me, stood in the doorway.

The old man said, 'Sorry, Freddie. I thought, you know, night's shades are falling fast.'

His accent was strange to me. He wasn't a Tynesider.

Uncle Freddie said, 'Come on in, Bob.'

The intruder hesitated to enter.

'I could come back later.'

'No need, man. Come on in,' my Uncle insisted.

The old man came into the washhouse. He smelt of stale tobacco and the streets. I suspected he was a tramp and that Uncle Freddie was offering him the hospitality of the washhouse, which was a lot better than sleeping in a doorway.

My Uncle introduced me to this stranger.

'Bob, this is my nephew Lecky!'

The man shook me firmly by the hand. It was a large, strong, calloused hand.

'Glad to meet you, boy,' he announced, 'At your service. Robert Service.'

Uncle Freddie laughed and explained, 'That's his Sunday Name. Bob's a poet and a traveller. From Canada, the land of the maple leaf!'

Robert Service added, 'And a bum. That's Canuck for tramp. Seeking a roof over his head and your good Uncle here has been providing said roof.'

I was sitting silent, bewildered by this strange man from the Chilkoot Pass.

'Beaver got your tongue, boy?' he asked.

I shook my head and my Uncle explained, 'We were just enjoying one of life's awkward pauses.'

'How's that now?'

'Lecky here has just blown his father's head off and we're waiting for the blood to dry,' and added, 'But make yourself at home, Bob.'

'I'm much obliged,' said Robert Service.

'No bother,' replied my amiable Uncle, 'No bother. Lecky, you stay and keep Bob company. And mum's the word, mind? Not a whisper to the ladies.'

'My lips are sealed,' I replied.

'I'll tell you when it's safe to poke your head over the parapet.'

With these last words my Uncle closed the washhouse door behind him.

So I watched the old man make himself a bed from his blankets and pack on the copper cover and then pick out a coal from the dying fire with a wary hand to light his pipe.

Then he turned to me and said, 'Well, you've had a good look at me, son. Wha'd'y'think? Will I do?'

'I've always wanted to sleep on top of the copper,' I answered, 'but they wouldn't let me.'

The old man laughed and drew on his pipe.

'Well, here I am, sleeping on top of your stove. Is that all right with you?'

I nodded agreement and asked, 'You don't have an ash stick and all your worldly goods tied in a bundle in a red spotted handkerchief. Are you really a tramp, Mr. Service?'

He laughed again and said, 'That would be an English tramp. But, yes, I am a bona-fide bum.'

'But what are you doing here?'

The old man pulled on his pipe and the aromatic scent dispelled the smell of Carbolic soap.

'I go where the road leads.'

'But you're Canadian?'

'I'm just travelling through this land of strangers.'

'You're very welcome to our wash house,' I assured him, 'We're not strangers.'

'Thank you kindly,' he said, 'But I guess it's the dog house to you.'

'I don't know what you mean?'

'You're in bad odour with your father, I understand?'

I nodded. I was suddenly reminded of how unhappy I was yet the aroma of his pipe tobacco was somehow comforting.

'I don't mean to pry,' he suggested, 'but I was once a boy myself.'

When he smiled I knew he was speaking out of remembered unhappiness unhealed.

'He was very, very angry,' I answered, 'I wanted to give a silent cry of joy, but he shouted at me.'

Mr. Service said, 'It's a sad, but true fact of life that every boy fights with his old man.'

'They do?'

He nodded gravely at me and wagged his pipe to illustrate the integrity of what he was saying.

'It's the nature of the beast. Two male animals living in the same space? One growing stronger and the other growing older? It's an un-natural situation.'

'It is?'

'It's what drives a man on to do something in the world. To build his own life. To outdo his father. That's nature, red in tooth and claw.'

I considered this astonishing statement.

'What happened?' the old man asked, 'If I'm not poking my snout in where it's not needed.'

I shook my head.

'I don't want to talk about it.'

'I can comprendy that,' Mr. Service said.

He pulled on his pipe, releasing yet further clouds of aromatic magic that I breathed in deeply. I resolved as soon as I was twelve years old and therefore eligible to become a smoker as Uncle Freddie had said, I would take to the pipe, which not only released delicious-smelling smoke, but also was very useful for wagging at people in conversation. In this companionable silence Mr. Service asked, 'D'y'like poetry? Verse?'

'Some of it,' I agreed reluctantly, 'Some is hard to understand.'

'Poetry is a way of communicating. Sometimes it works when talking doesn't. Shall I try communicating with you, Lecky?'

'If you like,' I agreed, 'I don't mind.'

'Okay, here goes nothing,' the old man said, cleared his throat and began to recite,

In the strife of the battle of life
It's easy to fight when you're winning;
It's easy to slave, and starve and be brave,
When the dawn of success is beginning.
But the man who can meet despair and defeat
With a cheer, there's a man of God's choosing;

The man who can fight to Heaven's own height
Is the man who can fight when he's losing.'

It was in the candle-lit washhouse in Hurworth Place that my path crossed that of Robert William Service, poet and world traveller, who came to sleep on our cooling copper. That night I decided to become a poet, a tramp and a traveller. I sat enthralled as the poet recited his encouraging words on the upturned poss tub, drinking in every word.

The pipe in his hand became a banner, a bugle, a sword as he declared,

'Carry on! Carry on!
Fight the good fight and true;
Believe in yourself, greet life with a cheer:
There's big work to do and that's why you're here.
Carry on! Carry on!
Let the world be the better for you!'

When he finished I found myself applauding, flushed and invigorated. Out of the darkness of the day had come understanding and encouragement from this old man from Chilkoot Pass.

'Would you like to come to my party, Mr. Service?' I asked, 'You could recite some more poems?'

To have a real live poet at my party would be streets better than any conjuror.

Sixteen

WE DIDN'T RECEIVE MANY LETTERS at Number One, Hurworth Place. What came through our door were mostly communications from authority or unsought bills. We regarded the postman passing our door with the same sense of relief the Israelites felt when the dark angel passed over their sleeping babes. Therefore when Our Mam and I heard the click of the letterbox I sprang to our front window only to see the dreaded figure walking away.

'It's the postman, Our Mam!' I cried in alarm.

'Keep your voice down,' she said, 'You'll wake your Dad.'

'What're we going to do?' I asked.

My Mother recovered herself.

'Well, we can't leave it lying on the mat.'

'We could,' I said, 'We could pretend it never came.'

'Don't be silly,' she said, 'Of course, we can't.'

She stood in thought for a moment and then asked, 'Can you think of anybody who would send us a letter? We're not behind with the rates,' and then, 'You haven't been sending off for catalogues again, have you?'

'No!' I responded indignantly, 'Not for ages.'

Occasionally we received through the door an invitation to send for Littlewood's or the Empire catalogue that I knew my Mother longed to see, but pretended for my Father's sake, to abhor. Fortunately Mrs. Richardson received lots of letters, some from foreign climes, and would always give me the envelopes. She believed I was a stamp collector and rather wished such a top-drawer hobby might rub off on Norman. I would soak off the least marked three-ha'penny stamp and with a lick of condensed milk send off my application for the latest catalogue. It never failed and my Mother and I enjoyed many happy hours window-shopping the unattainable.

'It could've been put through our door by mistake,' I suggested.

'Are you going down to get the letter or do I have to do it myself?' my Mother demanded.

I went down the stairs to the bottom landing and paused.

'Go on!' my Mother urged in a stage whisper from the top of the stairs.

I continued down the stairs to the bottom passage. There was an envelope lying on the scrubby mat behind the door.

I walked to the front door and picked up the letter. It was a brown envelope addressed to Mr. and Mrs. D. Ferguson. I carried it upstairs and surrendered it to my Mother. We went into the Room and closed the door. My Mother sat down in the Best Chair to open the envelope and read the letter.

I studied her face, but could make nothing from her sober expression.

'What does the letter say, Our Mam?'

'Will you give me a chance to read it first?'

I waited in an electric silence. My Mother started to read the letter aloud.

'Mr. and Mrs. David Ferguson and their son Alexander are invited to attend an interview at Jarrow Grammar School'.

'Oh, golly gum drops!' I interrupted.

She glared at me and continued, 'To ascertain Alexander's suitability as a candidate for the forthcoming annual Scholarship Examination.'

'What does that mean?'

My Mother said, 'They want to look at the whole bunch before they'll buy a banana.'

'It doesn't, does it?'

'We'll have to keep you at the school at least until you're sixteen,' she explained, 'Not every Mam and Dad can afford to do that. They need a wage coming in from their son. The school wants to make sure we're the right kind of people.'

'But we're not the right kind of people! Our Dad's threatening to have my guts for garters when he gets me on my own!'

'That could be a handicap when it comes to playing Happy Families,' she said, thoughtfully.

'What if he won't even come with us, Our Mam?'

My Mother said determinedly, 'He'll do what he's told for once.'

I was sobered and saddened.

'He never does what he's told for once. I know him. He'll spoil it like he spoils everything.'

'You sound just like your father,' said my Mother.

Inspired, I suggested, 'If he won't come with us, we could tell them he sends profuse apologies, but he's got his foot caught in the mangle and can't get away for love nor money.'

She took me by the ear and shook my head from side to side.

'That's exactly what I mean! Stop it! That sort of nonsense has to stop. Do you understand me?'

The Room door opened and my Father came in, chink, chink, dressed in his trousers, but no shirt.

He demanded, 'Don't tell me! Let me guess! Either we've declared war on Germany or this one's running off to Gretna Green to marry Miss Macaroni! Which one is it?'

I looked at my Mother and cried, 'Then you talk about me?'

She said, 'Go and get dressed, Davie. Then I'll let you read this letter.'

Seventeen

I WAS DREAMING I WAS SAILING in the scholarship, white sails flying, sky as blue as iris flags. Charlotte stood in the bow, laughing, pointing at the escort of dancing porpoises. It was a moment of supreme happiness. But then a dark cloud crossed the sun and Norman Richardson was with Charlotte, his arm about her waist, basking in the sunlight of her smile and there was a voice in my ear.

'Lecky! Wake up, old sausage!' Uncle Freddie urged.

I stirred drowsily and mumbled, 'Norman's holding Charlotte's hand.'

Uncle Freddie suggested, 'Only a dream, old sausage. Come on! Wake up!'

I came awake to protest, 'Uncle Freddie? It's Sunday!'

'Let's have you out of bed,' he insisted.

I started to rise, still sleep-ridden, complaining, 'What'm I going to do about Norman?'

Uncle Freddie pulled my nightshirt over my head.

'Hold your arms up!'

I obeyed and he stifled me in my shirt.

'Are we going fishing?'

Uncle Freddie stepped back.

'Something like that. Come on. Get your trousers on. You can do your boots downstairs.'

'Where're we going?'

Uncle Freddie handed me my boots.

'Wait and see. And hush, don't wake your mother.'

Before I'd taken a full breath we were walking up Albert Road in a silence I'd never experienced. The whole world except us two and a dew-furred cat were asleep. Nothing was stirring. Jarrow was waiting for the day to begin.

'Where're we going?'

My peerless Uncle replied, 'We're off to see what your father gets up to on a Sunday morn.'

'The bakery? He won't want to see me there,' I protested.

'We'll take good care he doesn't,' said my Uncle mysteriously.

When we entered the bakery back door it was to breathe that ethereal smell of bread, truly the staff of life. The lingering aftertaste of burning coke and tobacco, of flour and men, of yeast and boiled sugar filled any gaps in the rainbow. Already the heart of the bakery was beating as the rhythmic pulse of a dough-kneading machine, the rattle of bread tins and the voices of men made plain.

Uncle Freddie said, quietly, 'Now just stand still and watch.'

We stood in the shadow of the doorway, drinking in the scent of raw bread, staring at the wall of open mouths of the great ovens.

I asked, impatiently, 'What'm I watching for?'

'Just watch,' he said.

As I watched, a man, dripping with sweat, gasping for breath, crawled from one furnace oven mouth, brush in hand. Yeast bags were bound to his knees and elbows.

I started in surprise and Uncle Freddie holding me by the elbow, said, 'Shush!'

The man wiped the running sweat from his brow, gathered a grateful breath and hoisted himself into the next dragon's mouth. It was my father.

'Ecce homo!' Uncle Freddie declared, 'Behold the man!'

'Our Dad,' I gasped.

Into my ear, my Uncle said, 'Now have you the measure of the man?'

'But why does he do that?' I asked.

'No bread's baked on a Saturday night so the fires are banked down. Sunday morn's the only time the ovens are scarcely bearable for a man to crawl in and sweep them out.'

'I never knew.'

'There's no rush for the job. But your Mam needs the two shillings,' he explained, 'D'y'know what they call your father here?'

I shook my head.

'The Tin Man. They think because he's got a tin leg the rest of him doesn't hurt. And he's daft enough not to let on. That is the measure of the man.'

Years later I learned how the loudest of the hands, Archie Bragg, had gone to the manager, to insist a one-legged man shouldn't earn the same as a two-legged baker. Our Mam stitched his Military Medal – For Bravery in the Field – to Our Dad's apron to shame them and forced him to wear it for a week. So my Father's money was made up by his Sunday morning torment sweeping out the ovens with a hand brush. Our Mam needed those two shillings.

I sometimes wonder why we created such drama for ourselves, but ritual is essential to all societies, even one so minuscule as the Fergusons and Deans of Hurworth Place. And so this particular game was played out with my Father and I marooned on the landing and my Mother and Auntie Bella in the Room.

My Mother called to us, 'Are you two not ready yet?'

Auntie Bella added her twopennorth.

'Come on! We're waiting for the fashion show here.'

My Father put his mouth to the panel of the door as if his voice might not be powerful enough to penetrate to the Room.

'I've been standing on the landing forever. It's him that's messing about,' he bellowed, rattling the door in its frame, turning a disparaging eye upon me, being the him that was messing about.

Our Mam called, 'Get yourselves in here for inspection now.'

My Father opened the door and we entered the Room, suitably

creaking in our new boots. The ladies eyed us dispassionately.

'Well, what d'you think, Bella?' my Mother asked.

My dearest Aunt was suitably impressed.

'Champion! They look very smart to me.'

I complained, 'These boots creak, Our Mam!'

'All boots creak when they're new. That's how you know they're new, daftie!'

Auntie Bella added, 'There's many a one'll envy you, Lecky. New boots and not even Easter!'

Adding his own touch of jollity, Our Dad said, 'Aye and the tallyman'll still be round the doors next Easter and likely Easter after.'

Only to be reprimanded by Our Mam with a chiding, 'Don't spoil everything, Davie. Let's have a bit pleasure.'

Auntie Bella, a loyal sister, said, 'You look grand, Davie. Doesn't he, Mary?'

My Mother accepted the compliment gracefully.

'He's always been a handsome man. But it's rare he gets a chance to show it.'

'I'm not a slice of bread, Mary,' Our Dad pointed out rather obviously.

'What's that mean?' she asked suspiciously.

To which he said, 'You're wasting your time buttering iss up' which I thought was pretty smart.

Only for Our Mam to cap him by saying, 'Except I wasn't finished what I was saying. It's only a shame he's got that scowl riveted on his face.'

I thought that was very funny, but Our Dad didn't, transfixing me with said scowl.

Auntie Bella had given my Father a thorough inspection and asked, 'Is that the suit Tommy Makepeace was laid out in?'

My Father stiffened and said, 'I sincerely hope not.'

'No. He had the two. He went off in a clerical grey,' my Mother reassured him, 'I'd've preferred the grey, but his brother spilt a glass of port over him at the wake.'

My Father was not deeply reassured and a terrible thought struck me.

'This is not a dead boy's suit, is it?' I asked, suddenly uneasy.

'Don't be such a cowardy-custard,' my Mother accused me, 'You're lucky to have it! It's almost brand new. When Mrs. Callaghan's Ronnie came out of hospital the car driver paid for a new suit for him. I defy you to find the tears in those trousers where the car went over poor Ronnie!'

My Father and I exchanged glances of fellow feeling.

'Well, isn't anybody going to say if I look nice in this suit that was run over by a car?' I asked.

My beloved Auntie Bella hastened to compliment me.

'Of course, you do, pet! A perfect prince!' and kissed me on the brow.

'The handsomest of the Fergusons,' my Mother added, with a loving smile that my Father soured by adding, 'Which isn't saying much!'

Auntie Bella, exasperated, slapped him on the arm.

'Oh, Davie, spit something nice at your son just for once!'

My Mother turned on my Father to say, 'Stop it now, Davie! This is a very important day in our lives. Our son is going for an interview at the Grammar School.'

The dream shone bright in her workworn face. The chance of a job where her son didn't freeze or burn. The hope of indoors employment instead of sodden through to the skin, labouring in the rain. A railway clerk with a pocket watch and a pension. A person to be looked up to in celluloid collar and cuffs. She had worked miracles to find us suitable suiting in a matter of days with little to spend and new boots to buy.

'Now, no more carryonski!' my Mother ordered, 'Stand up straight and let's look at the pair of you. What d'you think, Bella? Will they pass muster?

'They're a credit to you, Mary,' my dear Aunt agreed.

My Mother fixed a stern gaze upon my Father.

'If you have to sign anything, Davie, don't stick your tongue out.'

My Father said, humbly, 'I can't help it if I'm concentrating.'

'You can very well help it. Keep your gob shut.'

She turned to her sister, and said, 'The finishing touch, Bella, if you, please!'

'I'm already finished,' my Father complained.

'I'm lending you both one of Mr. Forrester's silk handkerchiefs,' my Mother explained, and flourished two fine white silk handkerchiefs before our very eyes.

'Dapper!' I cried, 'They've got an F on them!'

Each handkerchief bore an elaborate F in one corner.

Auntie Bella explained, 'Which can as easily stand for Ferguson.'

'Or fathead,' my Father grumbled.

I reached for my delicate confection.

'I'll sample mine now!' I cried with due enthusiasm.

'No, you won't!' Auntie Bella protested, 'These are for show, not blow!'

'In your breast pocket. Like this,' my Mother said arranging the handkerchief as I squinted down my nose to see the effect, 'Just showing the initial. Very top drawer. But not for you to blow bogies into! Is that understood?'

'Yes, Our Mam!'

'And not for you to clean your lugs out either, Davie!'

The two familiar angels gave us one last inspection and nodded approval one to the other.

'Right! Now get yourselves down the yard. And no unseemly splashes on those trousers, thank you very much!'

My parents sat on uncomfortable wooden chairs in the paneled study of the Headmaster of Jarrow Grammar School while Mr. Turnstone himself lounged in a comfortable chair behind his desk. The wooden chairs creaked if my Mother or Father so much as twitched and the Headmaster would pause in his oration to look at them with obvious irritation.

I stood before his desk with my knees aching as I braced my legs to stand fast as the soldiers had stood fast unto death on the deck of the sinking Birkenhead. 'Remember the Birkenhead!' my Mother had whispered to me as Mr. Turnstone invited my parents to sit and me to stand before him. But I suspected the heroes of the Birkenhead would've broken ranks if they'd had to endure such a peroration as the Headmaster delivered to us, his hapless audience.

Hopefully drawing to a close, Mr. Turnstone said, 'A Grammar School course is not something to be undertaken lightly. It is not only intellectually arduous, but the temptation to withdraw a child at the age of fourteen for the sake of a wage often arises and must be resisted by the parents.'

Despite my Mother pinching his leg, my Father said, 'It's not our custom to break our word once given.'

'Quite. Quite so,' said Mr. Turnstone, approving the sentiment, and turning to me, 'Now, Alexander!'

I braced myself for a discussion of the Albigensian Heresy or the War of the Spanish Succession. Both my knees now bent as easily backwards as they did forwards.

'Yes, Mr. Turnstone.'

The Great Man asked, 'If I were to ask you what was your greatest ambition in life, how would you answer me?'

I stood silent, pondering the question.

'Well, boy?'

I said, 'You said if you were to ask me. I was waiting for you to ask me.'

'What is your greatest ambition in life?' asked the Headmaster.

'That's easy,' I said brightly, 'I want to be a tramp like Mr. Service.'

My Mother cried out her distress, 'Oh, Lecky!'

I continued, 'and travel round the world and be a poet.'

Mr. Turnstone gamely clutched at straws.

'A poet! Ah! Yes! "What is this life"'

I completed the line for him.

'If full of care we have no time to stand and stare?'

The Great Man contemplated me for a moment, and then said, 'Omnium rerum principia parva sunt.'

I felt he deserved an answer so I said, 'I thought all the poets were dead, but they're not. Did you know that, Mr. Turnstone?'

His face almost smiled and he replied, 'I had heard a rumour.'

I admitted, 'It was quite a shock to me. But Mr. Service is alive and kicking like a mule and although he admits himself he has become a mite careless of his visceral resonances which may be inappropriate for the genteel drawing room, it's just dandy for keeping the grizzlies at a respectful distance.'

The silence of incomprehension as the dust of centuries fell upon the study.

I said, 'It comes from living on a diet of beans.'

This simple explanation was followed by a silence broken only by the creaking of two pairs of new boots.

The Headmaster said, 'Quite. Now, Alexander, I'm going to ask you some simple questions. Please think before you answer. What is wrong with this sentence? King Charles walked and talked two hours after his head was cut off.'

I considered this implausibility.

'King Charles walked and talked. Full stop. Two hours after, comma, his head was cut off..'

'Can you tell me where three hundred Spartans defied two hundred thousand Persians?'

'In the Pass of Thermopylae,' I answered, '*Where we drew our cloaks about us and waited for the dawn and the coming of the Persians.*'

'In the Pass of Thermopylae,' the Great Man suggested, 'would have been a sufficient answer. What is the interest on £1,200 at six per cent for six months?'

I took a moment to think before answering, 'Thirty six pounds. You don't think six per cent is a bit greedy?'

Mr. Turnstone turned to my parents. My Mother looked almost tearful and the vein was throbbing in my Father's neck. They awaited the Headmaster's verdict with trepidation.

The Oracle spoke, 'The boy would appear to have been adequately instructed. Ficus ficus, ligonem ligonem vocat. But he's none the worse for that.'

My Mother sighed with relief and said, 'Thank you, Mr. Turnstone.'

To which he replied, 'Perhaps he may change his mind about becoming a tramp, Mrs. Ferguson?'

'Oh, I do hope so!' my Mother exclaimed, 'I'd like him in a clean shirt.'

The Headmaster turned again to me and asked, 'Now, Alexander, would you favour us with a recitation? Please begin in your own time. Festina lente!'

I cleared my throat and began vigorously,

> '*A bunch of the boys were whooping it up in the Malamute saloon,*
> *The kid that handles the music box was hitting a ragtime tune,*
> *Back of the bar, in a solo game, sat Dangerous Dan McGrew,*

And watching his luck was his light-o'-love, the lady that's known as Lou,
When out of the night, which was fifty below'

'Stop! Stop, this instant!' shouted an enraged Mr. Turnstone.

'Oh, Lecky!' my poor Mother cried again in anguish.

My Father's contribution was to state, 'I told you so! Didn't I tell you so?'

When the hubbub of horror abated, the Headmaster asked, 'What is this nonsense, boy?'

I protested, 'It's not nonsense, Mr. Turnstone. It's a poem called *The Shooting of Dan McGrew.*'

'Where on earth did you find this vulgar doggerel?' he demanded.

'It isn't vulgar, sir,' I explained, 'There's not a rude word in it from beginning to end.'

'You didn't learn it in school?'

'Mr. Service taught it to me.'

Mr. Turnstone sighed.

'And who is this Mr. Service?'

'Mr. Service is a famous poet who sleeps in our washhouse.'

At that moment my Mother exploded.

'In our wash house? Sleeping in our washhouse? This is the first I've heard of it!'

At that moment I knew I had betrayed my mother's dream. I would never be the railway clerk, hair glistening with brilliantine, snug behind three inches of solid oak with his shiny brass kettle singing on the stove behind him that my Mother prayed for me to become.

Eighteen

ALL THE WAY HOME MY FATHER and I sniped at one another.

'Well, that's put the kybosh on the Grammar School,' he announced with malign satisfaction.

'I didn't want to go anyway,' I retorted with an aching heart.

'Well, you're not going to get the chance,' he pronounced.

'I never wanted to go in the first place. So there!' I answered him.

My poor Mother turned on both of us.

'Stop it! Stop it, the pair of you! You're driving me out of my mind!'

She didn't try to hide her tears because it was raining and no one could tell tears from raindrops.

'I'm sick to death of the sight of both of yi!' she anguished. She turned and walked away, leaving us standing like lamp posts. We were too ashamed even to look at one another. We trailed home like beaten dogs.

The rain didn't stop all evening. It was as if the world were weeping. Nobody in our house was speaking to anyone else. Therefore it was a surprise to seek sanctuary in the washhouse and find Robert Service already in occupation.

He explained, 'Your saintly mother, God bless her, said she couldn't turn even a mangy chien out on a night like this.'

It seemed a golden world in the candlelight of the washhouse with the rain rattling like shrapnel on the slates.

'Take me with you tomorrow?' I suggested.

He looked at me and said, 'Today wasn't a splendid success?'

I hesitated to tell him, but he deserved an answer.

'He said *The Shooting of Dan McGrew* wasn't poetry. It was vulgar doggerel.'

'Tell me something new,' Robert Service said and smiled, 'But it's sure surprising how many people enjoy a rendering.'

'So I'm not going to the Grammar School,' I told him, 'And worse, Our Mam's not speaking to me either.'

We sat in a sympathetic silence as the rain beat its unceasing tattoo on the washhouse roof.

'If I tell you a brighter day will dawn, you won't believe me. So I won't try,' the poet said, 'Perhaps I can communicate better with a poem?'

I brightened at the prospect of a poem read by the poet. You had to hear the man to feel the magic.

'Tell me again the poem that Uncle Freddie likes so much.'

'Surely,' said the poet.

Robert Service began to speak and transported me from our shabby washhouse to a land of even grimmer prospect, but the words encapsulated such courage and resolution that even the faint heart of a child would be stirred.

The poet declared,

> *'I see across the shrapnel-seeded meadows*
> *The jagged rubble-heap of La Boiselle;*
> *Blood-guilty Fricourt brooding in the shadows,*
> *And Thiepval's chateau empty as a shell.*
> *Down Albert's riven streets the moon is leering;*
> *The Hanging Virgin takes its bitter ray;*
> *And all the road from Hamel I am hearing*
> *The silver rage of bugles sadly play*
> *Across the des'late headstones, line on line*
> *Of all those gallant boys from banks of Tyne.'*

We sat in silence as the bugle notes died away, but the remembrance of those gallant boys sacrificed for a hundred yards of bloody mud resonate forever.

'Well, now then, Lecky, mon vieux copain, was that doggerel or was that poetry?'

'That was poetry, Mr. Service,' I agreed wholeheartedly.

I was sitting on the top step of our stairs gazing through the lower landing window at the grey day beyond while a family conference progressed in the Room. I could hear the wordless voices as thunder rumbling beyond the river, the storm moving south to wash the thin streets of Jarrow of everything but unhappiness.

The Room door opened and my Mother said, 'Get yourself in here, Socrates!'

I hesitated to obey.

'You're going to have me adopted?'

'No!' she said, 'Who'd have you?'

'If you're going to send me on the Empire Scheme, I'd rather go to Australia than South Africa. I'd quite like a kangaroo for a pet.'

'I'll give you kangaroos!' she cried, 'if you don't get yourself in here!'

'If I have to join the Navy would you give me a note getting me off climbing up the mast?'

My Mother seized me by the ear and pulled me into the Room.

'One day,' I complained, 'My ear's gonna come off and then you'll be sorry.'

In reply my Mother seized me by the ear again and shook my head from side to side.

'Stop the nonsense!' she ordered, 'We want to talk to you.'

The magistrates were my parents, Auntie Bella and Uncle Freddie.

Auntie Bella said, 'Don't look so worried, pet.'

My Mother said, 'Freddie's told us about this daft idea of a party in the wash house on Saturday.'

Such a betrayal was a grievous blow. I looked at him with contempt.

'I won't ever tell you anything secret again, Uncle Freddie,' I said sadly.

'Sorry you feel like that, old sausage,' he replied.

I turned on my Mother.

'I've told Charlotte there's going to be a party, Our Mam. What'm I going to do when she turns up? You'll have to tell her, not me. I'll be hanging from the bannisters. You'll just have to push past my dead body and tell her, sorry, he's not here.'

To which my Mother replied, 'Sit down and don't talk so daft. Your father's got something to say to you. Haven't you, Davie?'

My Father, looking as if a certain somebody had had a few words with him, announced to my surprise, 'I think, and your Mam thinks as well, mebbes, you should have this lass, Charlotte, to tea on Saturday, eh?'

I was completely confounded. All the ice that had built up around my heart began to melt and my eyes were filled to overflowing.

'Well, say something!' my Mother urged.

'Aren't you going to say anything?' asked Auntie Bella.

I found voice enough to say, 'I'm giving a silent cry of joy.'

'And I thought it was constipation,' said my Mother.

My Father said, sternly, 'But only the little lass, mind you. We cannot be doing with a big party.'

'Oh, thank you, Our Dad, thank you very much!'

'I'll have a look-see at the bakery for a cake,' he admitted grudgingly, 'But I'm not promising anything.'

Auntie Bella hastened to say, 'Your Mam and me'll put together a nice tea, pet, you'll see. None better.'

Suddenly it was all too much for me and I began to weep tears of joy.

'Now what's he crying about?' my Father complained, 'Bubbling like a lass!'

My Mother chided him with, 'Oh, Davie, have a bit heart, man!'

'If he's to be a man he cannot keep bursting into tears!'

Through my tears I shouted at him, 'You're wrong! Mr. Butcher cried when his mare Queenie died! I saw him! And he was at Gallipoli. But he cried, as any decent man would do when Queenie died.'

My Father looked totally bewildered, but Uncle Freddie knew what I meant.

'So I can cry when I'm happy!'

Auntie Bella said, 'Come here, lamb, come here. Let's see what a hug'll do.'

My Mother said, 'I think we've made a mistake not sending you to Australia.'

Nineteen

IT SEEMED AN ENDLESS AGE UNTIL that particular Saturday dawned. I was dispatched downstairs while a considerable fuss was enacted upstairs. At last when my nerves had been stretched to breaking point I was allowed upstairs where Auntie Bella opened the Room door and ushered me in to where a feast fit for Scheherazade lay awaiting my inspection.

'Oh, Our Mam!' I cried, 'The table looks wonderful!'

'Didn't I tell you?' Auntie Bella rejoiced.

'Just you keep your mitts off,' my Mother counselled.

Auntie Bella reassured her.

'He won't touch, will you, pet?'

I marveled at the lavish spread.

'Four different jellies!'

My Mother explained, 'Well, they're all the same really, but it's amazing what your father can do with a little cochineal. Anything that's not got toothmarks all over Mrs. Porter'll take back.'

As I walked around the table my boots creaked. I'd grown used to this musical accompaniment to my progress, but Auntie Bella said, 'It's a pity about his boots, Mary. We should've done something about the squeak.'

'I think we've done enough, don't you?'

I supplied, 'If Granny was here she can get the squeaks out. I've seen her. She takes newspaper and dips it in the chamberpot and stuffs the boots with the wet paper.'

My Mother was slow to interrupt me.

'Then I'm just as happy she's not here. I know exactly how your Granny de-squeaks boots, thank you very much. The problem is how to get the smell out afterwards.'

Auntie Bella took over the role of etiquette adviser.

'Now remember, Lecky, pet, when you bring your guest to the table, you take the chair out for her and slide it back as she sits down.'

My Mother added, 'Your Dad'll do no more than look in to say hello to Charlotte. He won't interfere.'

'I think he's curious to have a look at her,' suggested my amiable Aunt.

'Then he's away down to Freddie,' my Mother explained, 'Once you two are settled, Bella and me'll slide off into the kitchen.'

It seemed to me the Room was lit with heavenly light and scented as the Gardens of Paradise. A sudden anxiety struck me.

'Do I look all right? Really alright?'

I was wearing my run-over-Ronnie suit and a tie of the Royal Antediluvian Order of Buffaloes that Mr. Chamberlain had been given by a companion in distress in the police cell who wished to appear anonymous before the magistrates. Mr. Chamberlain donned the tie before being brought up and was surprised to be awarded five shillings from the Poor Box and a kindly homily from the magistrate on the vicissitudes of life. Mrs. Chamberlain hoped I would enjoy the same good fortune.

Auntie Bella assured me, 'You look very handsome. D'y'remember the young Prince in THE HAND OF DEATH? You look just like him. Only, of course, he was blond and blue-eyed and taller than you, but otherwise.'

I said, 'I think I'll go down and wait for her.'

'It's only twenty to three,' my Mother said.

'I want to be ready.'

Auntie Bella warned me, 'She won't be on the dot.'

'Doesn't matter,' I said.

My heart was beating so fast I couldn't sit still.

My Mother and Auntie Bella listened to my creaky boots descending the stairs.

'Young love, eh, Mary?' said Auntie Bella.

'Well, he's certainly getting dafter,' her sister assured her.

Uncle Freddie was sitting on a kitchen chair outside their front door. I joined him to stand beside him, keeping clean, with my eyes peeled on Albert Road.

'There you are, old sausage,' he said, and then, 'I'm sorry for telling them what you'd planned. But it come out right, didn't it?'

'I'm sorry for saying I wouldn't tell you anything again.'

'Then we're quits?'

'Yes.'

'Good!' he said, 'I'd be very sorry if we weren't good friends.'

'We will be forever,' I assured him.

We shared a companionable silence listening to the utilitarian song of Albert Road, of people, carts, lorries, dogs and steam engines.

I confessed, 'I've written a poem about Charlotte.'

Uncle Freddie was pleased.

'Have you now? Bob sparked you off, eh?'

'I knew I was going to be a poet.'

'Anybody could see that,' he agreed.

'Only Mr. Service showed me it wasn't high faluting, but about ordinary life. He said, *Poetry is not the privilege of kings, but the true voice of the people.*'

'Well, let's hear it then!'

'Promise you won't laugh?'

'Is it meant to be funny?' he asked.

'No. It's deadly serious.'

'Then I won't laugh,' he assured me.

It was one of the moments in life to be remembered forever, standing outside Hurworth Place, reciting one of the earliest poems I ever wrote.

'All right. Here goes nothing,' I proclaimed and began,

> *'I love Charlotte MacAtominey.*
> *Her father keeps a butcher shop.*
> *Charlotte has a Shirley Temple coat*
> *There are kidneys on his chops.*

I love Charlotte MacAtominey
One day I hope we'll wed
Every night I say a prayer
For Charlotte in my bed.

But I know she'll never look at me
On her skates she whizzes fast
But I will love Charlotte MacAtominey
Until my life is past.'

When I'd finished there was silence. I found myself suddenly embarrassed and exposed.

'Well? Wha'd'y'think?' I asked, and as suddenly despondent, 'You don't like it.'

My meritorious Uncle assured me, 'I do like it,' and turning to look at me, 'Charlotte means a lot to you.'

'She means everything to me.'

My Uncle pondered a moment, and said, hesitantly, 'You mustn't expect too much of her, old sausage.'

'I don't,' I assured him, 'She's far above the likes of me.'

Uncle Freddie shook his head.

'That's not true. And you shouldn't even think it. But you won't believe me.'

'I know she is a Princess and I am of little account.'

'About the poem?' he suggested, 'Can you suffer a little criticism?'

'From you, yes, Uncle Freddie.'

'I just wonder about the word 'bed'? P'rhaps you could say? *'Every night I say a prayer for Charlotte in my head.'* You wouldn't necessarily be in bed, would you? And a poet should be truthful?'

I trailed upstairs as if climbing a treacle mountain and opened the door of the Room. My Mother and Aunt looked up at me expectantly.

'She's not coming, is she, Our Mam?' I reported despondently.

My Mother glanced up at the mantelpiece clock and said, 'It doesn't look like it. Seeing it's gone half four.'

Auntie Bella looked vainly for a glimpse of blue in a soot-sour sky.

She offered, 'P'rhaps there's been some misunderstanding?'

Grasping at straws, I suggested, 'She could've been taken desperately ill?'

'Then they might've stopped by with the ambulance and let us know,' my Mother commented sharply.

Auntie Bella hastened to suggest, 'I'm sure there's some simple explanation.'

We were mired in a slough of despond even deeper than Bedford Gaol. 'What should I do, Our Mam?'

Looking over the splendid feast bowing the legs of our table, she suggested, 'Well, seeing we have a table set for the Queen of Sheba, p'rhaps you should go round there and find out if the camels got lost?'

'Shall I come with you, pet?' asked Auntie Bella, rising from her chair. I shook my head.

'No, thank you. If it's something infectious we don't want to spread it.'

I walked downstairs with the heavy heart of a French marquis proceeding to an appointment with Madame Guillotine and walked out of the house. Uncle Freddie was talking to a passing postman. He called to me, but I didn't answer him.

All the way to Mr. MacAtominey's shop I prayed I would meet a flustered Charlotte hurrying towards me, apologising for being delayed because her Grandmother's goitre had fallen off. I would brush aside her apologies and hand in hand, we would skip happily back to Hurworth Place. However, there was no Charlotte hastening towards me and the butcher's shop bell struck a funeral note.

The shop was empty, but Mr. MacAtominey was hanging up fresh fly papers.

'Well, young man, I hardly recognised you,' he declared, 'What can I do for you today?'

I said, 'I came round to find out about Charlotte.'

Mr. MacAtominey took down a fly paper littered with insect corpses and replaced it with a fresh glutinous strand. On the discarded fly paper a bluebottle waved feebly at me.

'You know what you should do, young man?'

I stared at the dying fly signalling its desperate plight to me. Help me, help me, please!

'No, Mr. MacAtominey.'

The kindly butcher said, 'You should get yourself an appointments book. Then you'll be able to keep up with our Charlie and her flying circus.'

The fly gave a last flutter and was still forever. Mr. MacAtominey dropped the soiled strand into his waste bucket.

'She's not here?'

'You have to get your skates on to catch our Charlie,' her father declared.

I shook my head sadly.

'I haven't any skates.'

Mr. MacAtominey pulled out another gummy bandage from its cartridge and hung it on a hook in the window. A fly obligingly landed in the glue and struggled futilely to free itself.

'She's gone to the pictures,' he said, turning to me, smiling.

'Pictures?' I echoed, dismayed.

'With her little pal. What'shisname?'

'Norman Richardson,' I supplied.

'That's the one!' Mr. MacAtominey declared, 'They're away to the Kino.'

I turned on my heel to leave the shop and he called after me, 'You're a regular little toff today, son! Birthday, is it?'

The tolling of the funeral bell rang in my ears.

I climbed the stairs with an aching heart. My legs were leaden. My lungs laboured like Queenie on her last uphill travail. I had no idea how I was going to explain this heartless humiliation. But when I reached the top landing I was halted by astonishment. From the Room came the resonance of happy laughter. Was this the bitterest pill of all? Were they were laughing at my gullibility? I opened the door and stepped into the Room to face four happy faces.

'So he said to the pollis, 'Well, what would you do if you had a porpoise stuck up the chimney?' recited Uncle Freddie and all four adults burst into renewed laughter. As they fell about in mirth and mopped their eyes I stood enraged, an indignant ghost at the feast.

'What do you think you're doing?' I cried, hurt at such betrayal.

As the laughter subsided, my Mother said, 'What's it look like? We're having our tea.'

'Has she come?' I cried, suddenly liberated from my fly paper of despair.

'Has who come?' asked my Mother.

'Charlotte,' I said, 'Who else?'

Auntie Bella said, 'No, she hasn't, pet.'

She regarded me with sympathy.

'But this has!' my Father declared, waving a brown envelope in the air.

'What has?' I asked, bewildered.

Auntie Bella explained, 'Freddie brought it up. From the postman.'

My Father rapped on the table with a spoon and cried, 'A little hush and decorum, if you please!'

'What's happened?' I cried.

My Father surrendered the letter to my Mother who began to read aloud.

'Dear Mr. and Mrs. Ferguson, I write to inform you that your son, Alexander, will be admitted to the Scholarship Examination for entry to Jarrow Grammar School.'

My Mother sat at the table with tears of joy running down her face while Auntie Bella comforted her while wiping away her own tears. The men started singing, most inappropriately, banging spoons on the table, 'No more Latin, no more French, no more sitting on the hard school bench! No more stick and no more strap, no more sitting on the master's lap!' being the only jingle associated with school they recollected.

I remember standing there, heartbroken and heartlifted both, but I recall most clearly the happiness that illuminated that shabby room. I have not parted from these simple, loving people and they are not separated from me nor I from them ever.

Twenty

NEIGHBOURS ARE WHAT GIVE LIFE its particular flavour. Next door to the Fergies and the Deans in Hurworth Place lived the Chamberlains and they gave ample flavour to life, both sweet and sour.

Mr. Chamberlain was what my father described as a man who could sleep in a wheelbarrow. I presume he meant George Chamberlain was not the most diligent of men, but he seemed to me to be always on the move. He was a splendid runner and I remember one occasion on which he was being pursued by three men down Grange Road and yet outran all three, leaving them breathless, cursing and swearing in his wake.

On another occasion in our back lane he asked me to keep safe a small suitcase that had belonged to his dear departed Mother while he went to enquire the time from a policeman. I told him I'd go and see the time for him from Auntie Bella's clock, but he said, no matter, a policeman would turn up any moment soon and he'd ask the constable. I was most surprised when he was proved correct and a constable appeared; in fact, two policemen, one at each end of the back lane. Mr. Chamberlain went to ask the time of one constable and then Mr. Chamberlain and the constable went to consult with the second constable, doubtless to ensure the correct time was given.

When Mr. Chamberlain returned to claim his Mother's suitcase I asked him why his Mother hadn't taken the suitcase with her when she departed and he assured me it would be sent on. He said it contained items of sentimental value that his Mother treasured. This surprised me as childish curiosity had driven me to examine the suitcase contents, which turned out to be twenty-four tins of corned beef. I was left with the inescapable conclusion that the redoubtable Granny Chamberlain had departed to join a Polar expedition.

As a reward for looking after the old lady's suitcase Mr. Chamberlain gave me a pomegranate. As I was very young I didn't know what it was and worse, neither of us knew what to do with it. Ignorance was understandable on my part, but less so on Mr. Chamberlain's.

We tried biting through the skin without success. We tried bouncing it off the cobbles, as we would've done with a cocoanut. It simply bounced back. We finally solved the problem by hitting the pomegranate with Auntie Bella's poss stick. The tough skin split open and the pomegranate skidded away from under the poss stick. When we finally got the ruptured fruit out of the yard drain we were dismayed to find there were no juicy segments like an orange or tangerine, but a mass of small shiny berries sticking together that were difficult to pull apart.

We sat on our backyard doorstep together eating the berries one by one, but it was a big disappointment to us both. I suggested he return the pomegranate to the shop and retrieve his money, but he said, no, he would stand the expense, but let this be a lesson to us both, British is best. Just when we were at our most exasperated Ali Jamjar's cart turned into the lane and we fed the fatal fruit to Bucephalus who showed every evidence of enjoyment. Honour satisfied, Mr. Chamberlain shook hands with me and we parted company on good terms.

I was very fond of Mrs. Chamberlain. My Mother said our neighbours lived hand to mouth, which I interpreted in my literal fashion as the Chamberlains being short of cutlery. She was a large, cheerful woman who accepted adversity as an everyday commonplace and seemed never to despair in the face of persistent rent men, tallymen and assorted debt collectors. She lived by Micawber's law that something would turn up and was never disappointed. There was always a rent man, tallyman or debt collector turning up to bang on her front door.

'They're away to Whitley Bay,' my Mother would lie, 'They've taken digs for a fortnight at the Spanish City.'

Reading apparently was another popular destination for the Chamberlains.

'They've relatives in Faversham,' my Mother would recite barefaced and the tallyman would retreat, somewhat awed as Faversham sounded rather snobby.

'I wonder you're not ashamed,' my Mother would snap at the rent man, 'Persecuting decent people when there's a death in the family. They're away to Peterborough for the funeral.'

I suspect my Mother enjoyed her dramatic performances, which were much appreciated by Mrs. Chamberlain.

But I loved Mrs. Chamberlain particularly because we sang together. Our netties were wall to wall and when I sang, sitting on our wobbly wooden seat, Mrs. Chamberlain would sing with me. We sang all Shirley Temple's hits and the songs of our time, *Somebody Loves Me*, *Summertime*, *I Got Rhythm*, but our all-time favourite was *Red Sails In The Sunset*. We sang Red Sails with bursting hearts; the evocative loneliness of the song, the aching for love assured brought us close to tears. When we finished our short concert we would flush the netties and the rushing fall of water would be our applause as we stepped out into the rain or sunlight, separated only by a brick wall.

My father sang such songs as *Father, Fetch a Hammer*, *There's a Fly on Baby's Brow* and *Don't Pour the Po from the Window, Polly, Papa's Asleep on the Porch!* My Mother did not approve.

Mrs. Chamberlain had four sons, all older than me. They were called Matthew, Mark, Luke and John. She also had a daughter called Rebecca who was, surprisingly, only two years old with a gap of twelve years between Rebecca and John. When we were sitting out the front of Hurworth Place one afternoon, enjoying the sunshine and the song of the road, with Rebecca asleep in her Mother's lap, I asked her how it was that there was such a gap in age.

She told me she'd woken up one morning and there was this strange baby in bed with her. She said she'd asked George and he said it was nothing to do with him. He suggested she should put an advert in the paper to get shot of it, but no, she said, she'd got used to having the bairn in the house, so she'd just kept it. I thought at the time, looking upon the sleeping child, how lucky she was that Mrs. Chamberlain had decided to keep her; that she was with people who loved her.

Luke, or Lucky as our vernacular anointed him, was Mrs. Chamberlain's son that I had most to do with. Not that I wanted to keep company with him, but along with the more amiable John and other boys I would be recruited when he wanted to go hunting rabbits. Armed with half-bricks we would walk to the open fields at Simonside and systematically quarter the pasture in a line. We searched for isolated grass clumps where a rabbit would be hiding in its burrow, believing immobility was invisibility. The half-brick would be slammed into the burrow and the rabbit would squeal and dance on its nose until Lucky placed his boot on the unfortunate creature and broke its neck.

I hated the whole procedure and prayed ardently at every grass clump I approached that no rabbit would be in tenancy. If a rabbit bolted from under my feet Lucky would rage at me and threaten me with his half-brick. I truly believed that any second now he would beat me to the grass, place his great boot on the Fair Isle pullover Granny Fergie had knitted me and break my neck.

Thus I approached the fresh fields of Simonside in a state of near hysteria. The worst times were when Lucky decided I should be next in line to him. Which led to the terrible occasion when in a state of utter panic induced by Lucky's systematic slaughter of unoffending rabbits; as he approached me to shake another glassy-eyed coney under my nose I threw my missile into a wet cow pat which sprayed us both. I didn't stay to apologise, but ran for my life with rabbits bolting in all directions from burrows in my wild passage.

Lucky's rabbits were destined for his Mother's pot or to be sold for pennies to neighbours such as my Mother who was very grateful for fresh game. Unfortunately there were days when Lucky had promised his Mother or a neighbour fresh rabbit for the pot when no rabbit stayed to be bricked or the burrows were empty.

In those days many Jarrow households kept rabbits in the back yard as pets, but principally for the pot. On our way home from a fruitless hunt we would investigate the back yards until Lucky found a suitable rabbit happily munching a carrot in its hutch. He would then abduct, kill and skin the rabbit with astonishing speed and skill. Lucky often finished off the carrot as he finished off the unfortunate owner.

Then one of we unfortunates of his chain gang would be ordered, as a dare, to return the empty skin to the rabbit hutch. No one ever refused such a dare lest Lucky kill and skin the refusenik in the back lane there and then. Lucky's thinking was that anybody who discovered the empty skin of the family rabbit tastefully laid out in the hutch wouldn't connect its disappearance with Lucky sauntering up the back lane with a naked rabbit swinging from his hand.

Some years later Lucky's luck finally ran out when to avoid paying the fare he jumped off the tram travelling at speed and landed square in the path of a coal lorry.

We were all very sorry for Mrs. Chamberlain's distress. Mr. Chamberlain said Lucky had been the apple of his Uncle Tommy's eye and Tommy would've taken Lucky into business with him. Uncle Tommy unfortunately couldn't attend the funeral as he was detained on business abroad. We all knew Tommy Chamberlain was abroad, in prison on the Isle of Wight, sewing mailbags. Despite our concern for Mrs. Chamberlain there were those among us who weren't too grieved at Lucky's early departure from this vale of tears.

However, this is how it came about that on a certain Sunday morning the Fergusons sat down to enjoy rabbit and three veg in full family.

I remember, I remember the house where I was born, grew up and celebrated Sunday dinner. Sunlight and Sweet William on the kitchen windowsill. A linen snowfall blotting out our shabby table. My mother, glowing with happiness and my father just glowering. My sisters, Nancy and Peggy were home, released from Panhacklety House for a precious weekend of freedom.

But I had noticed my sisters were not the carefree girls they were once; no longer childish hands and wrists, but bigger, harder hands with a bracelet of chapped skin at the wrist, and Peggy, my younger sister, was thinner and quiet. Nancy more and more resembled my Mother, sinewy and capable; as if the dew of childhood were lost forever.

My Mother rejoiced in their company, disbelieving of their presence so much that she touched and laid hands upon her daughters as if to assure herself they were here in the flesh.

'Before your father carves,' she announced, proudly, 'Lecky'll say grace for us.'

My Father as was his nature instantly protested.

'When did we start having grace?'

'Since now we do,' my Mother challenged, and to me, 'Go on, Lecky!'

A humble silence fell upon our kitchen, heads were deeply bowed, almost into the gravy boat, palms pressed tight in supplication and my Father sighed deeply like an organ tone. In every Church there is always one Dissenter.

'Benedictus benedicat, per Jesum Christum, dominum nostrum. Amen,' I recited, self-consciously aware of a temporary elevation in status. Everyone politely chimed in with an Amen, but the open admiration on my sisters' faces was generous reward.

'And Benedict Arnold another bottle of beer no hope of Gordon Bennett, I suppose?' my Father proclaimed, but everyone ignored him.

'That's Latin. Benedictus,' my Mother explained to my sisters, 'We have a scholar in the house!'

The girls' eyes and mouths opened wide in astonishment.

Nancy cried, 'He's never won a scholarship!'

My Mother smiled proudly upon her.

'That's exactly what he has gone and done, Nancy.'

Peggy's moon face glowed with pride.

'Our Lecky going to the Grammar School?'

'I'm just worried,' my Mother confided, 'That he'll know it all before he gets there.'

'I'm just worried,' my Father contributed, 'that there might be a uniform still to pay for. And Godfrey knows what else.'

The females of the family sensibly ignored him, which only further exasperated my Father who emptied his few pennies from his pocket and counted them over and over sighing deeply.

Nancy said, proudly, 'You'll show us all up yet, Lecky,' with just a hint of wistfulness.

'No, I won't,' I said stoutly.

'Was the examination very hard?' Peggy enquired.

'You wouldn't believe it, Peggy,' I exclaimed, 'It was all about filling baths without putting the plug in!'

Peggy was astonished at such outrageous behaviour.

'What a disgrace! Her Ladyship throws a tantrum if we use even a drop of hot water!'

My Mother was concerned and asked, 'Oh, Peggy, that can't be true, surely?' even though her daughters' hands and wrists bore witness to the truth.

'And how long,' I declared, 'it would take two men and a boy to build a wall half a mile long.'

'Huh!' Peggy cried, 'If it was Panhacklety House they'd never finish. Mr. Beestie has to stand over them with a whip to get the men to do anything!'

'So when do you start at the Grammar School?' Nancy asked.

But before I could answer, my Father declared, 'So when do we have our dinners? If anybody's interested.'

My Mother rose and brought the rabbit on his bed of parsnips from the oven and Nancy brought the vegetables from the hob. The rabbit was placed in front of my Father.

'Hush!' my Mother said, 'Your father's gona sign his name!'

The Head of the Household picked up the carving knife and announced, 'Now afore I start carving.'

My Mother interrupted with, 'Now, don't start your nonsense, Davie, please!'

But it was too late. He had been slighted by the women monopolising the conversation and was not a man to be lightly slighted.

My father pulled the pin from his grenade and rolled it down the table. 'Before I start carving, does anybody here know this rabbit's name?'

We had played this game before, but not in the presence of my sisters since their transportation. To my living shame I joined in and answered, 'I think his name is Snowball, Our Dad!'

'Oh, Lecky!' my Mother cried.

'Would yi like me to say a few words before I dish Snowball out?' my Father enquired, smiling amiably round the table.

Peggy gave a heartrending scream. Her chair flew over backwards and she fled from the kitchen, slamming the door behind her so hard the latch fell on the floor.

This was a most ominous omen as the latch had only once before vacated its post when my Grandfather had declared he wasn't staying where he wasn't wanted and was off to the opal fields of Australia and not to send his post on. I was not allowed to go with him despite my pleas.

My Mother cried, 'Peggy! Come back here!'

The only response was the slamming of the bedroom door. A terrible silence prevailed in the kitchen. The ghost of Lucky Chamberlain smiled upon us.

My Mother said, wearily, 'Oh, Davie! Did you have to do that?'

'Just a bit joke,' my Father said defensively.

Nancy snapped, 'I don't call it a joke,' and to me, 'You're as bad.'

My Father said, 'She's ower sensitive.'

We sat in a sad silence. Then my Mother, rising to her feet, said, 'Well, at least she has got feelings, bless her,' and to my sister, 'Sit still, Nancy. I'll see to her.'

My Mother picked up the fallen latch, slipped it into the door and departed to comfort Peggy.

Twenty One

My Grandfather never reached the opal fields, but only Charlie's field by St. Paul's Church from whence he was returned to us by the police, stinking of red biddy. The Vicar generously refused to press charges against the old man. On being refused permission to sleep in the church my Grandfather had chased the Vicar round the nave, pelting him with hassocks and offering to fight him with one hand tied behind his back until the unfortunate man had been forced to lock himself in the vestry. My Grandfather drank the Communion wine from the sacristy and retired to sleep under the stars on Charlie's field. To sleep under the stars on Charlie's field with the song of the river in my ears is something I wish I had experienced.

The silence lasted forever only to be broken by Nancy who accused my Father, 'Just this once, Our Dad, couldn't we have had our dinners in peace?'

My Father unfortunately answered, 'Oh, you'll all get a 'peace' right enough.'

Desperate to lighten the atmosphere, I urged Nancy, saying, 'That's called a pun, Nancy. D'y'gerrit? Peace and piece?'

She ignored me.

'It's not funny, Our Dad.'

My Father knew he had behaved badly but persisted with, 'But a rabbit's not an octopus, y'know. Somebody'll have to have the ears and tail.'

I was his steadfast accomplice.

'Why don't we get an octopus then, Our Dad?'

The latch lifted and my Mother came into the kitchen.

'She won't come back.'

My Father said, defiantly, 'Can we get on with our dinners then?'

My Mother sat down without responding.

'Oh, well, if that's the way the wind blows, I'll take mine into the Room,' my Father said.

With an icy chill, my Mother answered, 'You do that, Davie.'

My Father filled his plate, picked up his knife and fork and said, 'Next time I won't try to add to the air of jollity.'

My Mother sprang up like a tigress.

'What jollity, Davie?' she snarled, 'Your daughter's crying her heart out in the bedroom. In an hour she'll be gone back to that hellhole, but you don't care!'

My Father shuffled his feet. 'I do care,' he said and left the kitchen.

My Mother and Nancy served out our dinners in silence. Nancy took a plateful of dinner to the bedroom. When she returned she said, 'I don't know if she'll eat it.'

'P'rhaps we should get an octopus next time?' I suggested.

My Mother turned on me with the carving knife in her hand.

'If I were you I'd open my mouth only to eat.'

We sat down to eat and my Mother's wonderful dinner tasted like old straw.

'If we had an octopus we'd all get a leg,' I tried, hopefully.

'Do you want to eat out on the stairs?' my Mother suggested.

Nancy said, 'If I told them at Panhacklety what went on here nobody would believe me,' and shook her head sorrowfully.

'Tell them about our octopus,' I suggested, 'See if they believe that.'

'I'll octopus you in a minute,' my Mother responded automatically, and to Nancy, 'What time d'w'have to leave for the station?'

By Jarrow station there was a little pie shop whose proprietor fancied himself a poet and whose window displayed his latest offering advertising his wares. As my Mother walked arm in arm with Nancy and Peggy I memorised his latest epic. When I looked away from the window my Mother and sisters were gone.

I ran into the station just as the great, snorting, steamy, coaly beast grumbled to a halt. The doors sprang open and people, liberated, sprang to the platform, talking and chattering. For a moment I thought I had lost my Mother and sisters, but, no, there they were by the open door of a forward carriage as my Mother always advised; if the platform was short you might get carried past your destination. I arrived panting and breathless, almost carried beyond my destination by the urgency of my arrival.

'Peggy!' I cried, 'Wait! Wait for me!'

The porter blasted my eardrums with 'Newcastle train! Mind the doors, please! Newcastle train!'

I arrived to break up the last loving embrace.

'I want to say something!' I explained.

My Mother who was barely speaking to me snapped, 'If you must, but hurry up! Be quick about it!'

I seized Peggy's hand and recited, with fulsome passion, 'Farewell, farewell, for parting is such sweet sorrow, but don't forget that Gaudie's will have fresh pies again tomorrow!'

I smiled up at Peggy expecting at least a parting kiss, but instead my sister gave an unearthly shriek that chimed with the guard's whistle and the exasperated screech of the steam engine. Carriage doors slammed like an artillery salute.

To my bewilderment Peggy continued to shriek and my Mother snarled, 'Now look what yi've done! You great daftie!'

My sister wailed, 'I'm not going, Our Mam, I'm not! I hate it there! I want to stay with you!'

My poor Mother cried, 'Yi can't, pet. Yi have to go!'

Peggy clung to my Mother, pleading desperately, 'Please let me stay with you! Please!'

My Mother tried to coax her to enter the carriage.

'Come on, pet, be sensible!'

Peggy clung to the carriage door as a limpet to a rock, crying,

'Oh, Mam! Oh, Mam! Don't send me back! Please!'

It took the combined efforts of my Mother, Nancy and the porter, pushing and pulling, to propel Peggy onto that train. Even as the carriage door was closing on her, my sister cried, 'You don't know what it's like, Our Mam! I'll never be a bad girl again if you let me stay!'

The carriage door closed and we stood back, my Mother gasping for breath. The two girls wrestled beyond the glass as two butterflies in a killing bottle. I saw the anguish in Nancy's face reflected in the pain in my Mother's face as the train pulled slowly away, drowning Peggy's inaudible lament. I learnt then the bitter pain of parting that never ends.

My Mother stood gasping for breath. The old porter walked away, shaking his head. I wished I had never been witness to my sister's unhappiness.

When she had regained herself my Mother said, 'I cannot believe it!'

I said, 'I'm sorry,' but couldn't meet her eye.

'What made yi start her off?' demanded my Mother.

'It was in the pieman's window.' I offered.

'Gaudie's window?'

We stood in silence.

'But don't forget that Gaudie's will have fresh pies again tomorrow,' my Mother said in a voice so sad I felt the tears start. My Mother took out a handkerchief and wiped her eyes and blew her nose. She offered me the handkerchief, but I shook my head and blinked away my tears.

'Let's away home,' my Mother suggested.

As we walked I asked, timidly, 'Is it really that bad in Scotland?'

My Mother stopped, looked at me and considered her answer.

She said, 'When they teach you at the Grammar School about slavery, tell them you already know. Tell them your sisters are in service at Panhacklety House.'

From the distant ribbon of steel the voice of the train carrying my sisters to slavery echoed mournfully: the voice of pain and loss.

That night through the wall I heard my Mother weeping in her lonely bed. She wept for her brave Nancy and silly Peggy gone to the Big Hoose at Jedburgh-over-the-Border in rarified Roxburghshire. And no one could ever mend that hurt for her.

Twenty Two

WHEN WE HEARD THE DISCORDANT NOTE of a bugle carried on the breeze Uncle Freddie and I knew when we turned the corner of Edith Street who would gladden our morning. For there was in Bede's town when I was a bairn a certain Ali Jamjar, a rag and bone man, black as midnight, a mysterious princeling, resplendent in his velvet curtain cloak and towel turban with the Black Prince's ruby pinned to his brow.

As we turned into Edith Street a further bugle blast and a cry of 'Rag-a-bone!' greeted us. There sat Ali Jamjar on his cart with the long-suffering Bucephalus between the shafts, his ears still twitching from the last unmelodious blast.

Ali grinned at us and offered, 'How now, Freddie?'

'Fair to middling, Ali,' my amiable Uncle replied, 'How's business?'

Ali shook his head, easing aching shoulders.

'There's no business, Freddie. They've nowt to put out. Nowt to sell.'

There was very little on his cart. Even his coveted balloons seemed dispirited. His box of Lucky Bags was undisturbed.

'Sign of the times,' Uncle Freddie sympathised, 'But worse bad when a ragman cannot scratch a living.'

Ali agreed, 'It's niver been so bad,' and turning to smile at me, he asked, 'What's new with you, Lecky, son?'

I reported, 'Our Mam's thinking of getting us an octopus.'

Ali laughed and said, 'Your Mam was always one for novelties.'

'It's not a pet,' I assured him, 'We'll fatten it up for Christmas.'

'Now I niver knew,' Ali said with some surprise, 'Are they good to eat, these octopuddles?'

I assured him, 'Heaps better than a chicken. We'd all get a leg each. And then there's the ink.'

'Which remembers me,' Ali said, 'I hear you sail on a scholar ship.'

I was amazed and flattered that he knew of my success.

'Does everybody in the whole world know about my Scholarship?'

'Only us top drawer people. When I next gets something with the Latin on I'll get you to tell me what it says, professor?'

'You'll have to give me a week or two to get the hang of it, but when I do, I'll read anything for you!'

Ali smiled and said, 'I will count on that,' and picked up his reins. Bucephalus raised his head.

Uncle Freddie asked, 'Where you off then, Ali?'

'There's nowt in Jarrow. I shall go on circuit.'

'Judges go on circuit,' I remarked.

'Then why not a rag-and-bone-man?' Ali responded.

'Why not?' said Uncle Freddie.

As Bucephalus stirred himself I said, 'I wish I could come with you, Mr. Jamjar.'

'I'll send yous a postcard from Kelso, Freddie,' said the great man, and to me, 'Salve atque vale, filius Alexander!' He winked at me and clicked his tongue at Bucephalus who was already moving. The cart rattled away and Ali Jamjar raised the bugle to his lips to peel more pebbledash from the walls of Edith Street.

'That was Latin,' I said, somewhat surprised.

'Why should a rag-and-bone man not have a taste for Latin?' said Uncle Freddie, 'But there is one thing that Ali cannot do and that is play the bugle. No wonder the walls of Jericho fell down.'

We continued our meander down Edith Street towards Christ Church whose steeple points eternally to Heaven leading our gaze upwards from the gutter. I was engaged on a spiritual errand. At my Mother's behest I was on pilgrimage to say prayers for my sisters, Nancy and Peggy, as penance for causing the disturbance at the station when the girls returned to Panhacklety House. It wasn't that my Mother was particularly religious. She regarded the Church much as she regarded a visit to the panel doctor or Edie Hinds, the greengrocer. I might as well have been sent to have my ears syringed or for a pound of Brussels sprouts and a stone of potatoes.

As we walked I asked my Uncle, 'You've never told me how Mr. Jamjar got the Black Prince's ruby.'

'You wouldn't rather compose yourself for your act of contrition?' he suggested.

'I am composed,' I replied, 'I know what I'm going to say.'

'Well,' said my Uncle, 'it all started one Christmas Eve when Edward the Seventh and Kaiser Bill the Umpteenth were staying at Jarrow Hall with the Squire.'

This was the first I'd heard of this unexpected friendship.

'What were they doing there?'

'What royalty does best,' Uncle Freddie replied.

'What's that?'

'Cadging free bed, board and booze off folk gullible enough to provide it,' he informed me.

'They'd better not come round our house then,' I warned.

Uncle Freddie continued, 'Kaiser Bill always travelled with the German heavyweight boxing champion, Karl Kronstadt.'

'Why?'

'The Kaiser was a runty little pimple who preferred other people to do his fighting for him.'

'What about King Edward?' I enquired.

'He was a fat little blister who only wrestled with the fair sex.'

I digested this unusual information.

'You're not allowed to fight girls.'

My amiable Uncle explained, 'Teddy and Bill were sloshing their way through the Squire's wine cellar, no expense spared.'

I interrupted to ask, 'Didn't the Squire object?'

'He just kept saying . . . *As your Majesties pleases*. What else could the poor blighter say?'

Indignantly, I retorted, 'He could say, why don't you buy your own?'

'By the time they got to the tenth bottle, Kaiser Bill says, *I bet*, he says, *mein Karl could knock ten bells out of any Englander you could come up with.*'

'What a cheek!'

My Uncle continued, 'So Teddy says, *Rein back your reichmarks, Bill. I could walk out on to Church Bank right now and the first Englishman I see could knock eleven bells out of your turniphead.*'

I thoroughly agreed with the sentiment. British is best, as Mr. Chamberlain and I had both agreed, whether pomegranates or pugilism.

'*Donner und blitzen!* says Bill. *No, no*, says Teddy, *Play fair. One at a time. You're on, mein freund,* says Kaiser Bill.'

Uncle Freddie had me entranced with his fluent German and the gentlemanly tones of our own revered sovereign.

'So out goes Teddy with a footman holding a big brollie over him because it's snowing and the first pair of legs he sees is Ali Jamjar. Only, of course, his Gracious Majesty doesn't know it's Ali. *I say, chappie*, says his Royal Highness, *do you fancy going twelve rounds with the Heavyweight Champion of Germany?*'

I drew in a deep breath.

'That's an invitation it would be hard to refuse!' I exclaimed.

Uncle Freddie continued with his toe-gripping narrative, saying, 'Then, peeping out from under the brollie, His Gracious Majesty sees Ali is black. *Oh, no*, he says, *you're black. You're no good. What did you say?* asks Ali. *Are you deaf as well as black?* says Teddy, *I said, you're black. Don't pretend you're not. Black as the ace of spades. You're no good to me.*'

My beloved Uncle paused and drew breath having recreated for my singular benefit two dissimilar characters in a thespian mode Sir Henry Irving himself would've envied.

I shook my head and commented, 'I bet Mr. Jamjar wasn't pleased.'

'Ali flattened Karl Kronstadt flatter than the lino on the floor.'

I cried out in delight.

'Hoorah!'

'He terrified the Squire of Jarrow so much he ran half-way to Hebburn in his pyjamas.'

I decided, 'That'd teach him to grind the faces of the poor.'

'And he banged Bill and Teddy's nappers together so hard, that ever afterwards the Kaiser kept falling off his nag and bursting into tears. Thereafter Teddy had to be propped up with cushions and too often reminded what his name was.'

That seemed a satisfactory conclusion to me, but, I asked, 'But how did Mr. Jamjar get the Black Prince's ruby?'

Uncle Freddie said, 'It fell out of Teddy's crown when Ali banged their bonces together. Ali picked it up for safekeeping. He always meant to return it, but Teddy daresn't ask him for it back.'

We arrived at the door to Christ Church and Uncle Freddie stopped.

'Aren't you coming in?' I asked.

'It wasn't me that put poor Peggy in hysterics,' he replied.

'I thought you'd come in with me.'

'When He wants me God knows where I am,' my Uncle said, 'I'll wait for you here.'

So I went into the sanctified gloom of Christ Church. There were some old ladies in the front pews. I sat in the back pew and shuffled the hassocks around with my feet while I thought out what I was going to say to God. When I looked up there was a man in a long dark dress watching me. I wondered if he knew I was the grandson of the man who had chased the Vicar round St. Paul's.

He said, 'When you've finished playing football with the hassocks.'

'I wasn't playing football,' I answered.

'Then what're you doing here?'

'I came to say some prayers.'

He regarded me with some scepticism.

'Why?'

'My Mother sent me,' I replied.

He regarded me for a black eternity and then said, 'Well, get on with it. But I'll be watching you.'

I knelt down on a dusty hassock, breathed in damp and desolation and prayed for my sisters, Nancy and Peggy. It was an incoherent prayer interrupted by tears, but one note sounded urgently however hard I tried to suppress it.

When I got home my Mother was waiting for me. My depressed demeanour satisfied her that I had crawled every stony cobble to Canossa.

'Well?' she demanded.

'Well what?'

'Did you do it properly?'

'Yes.'

'What did you pray for?'

It was the inquisition I might expect returning from Edie Hinds with kale instead of cabbage.

'For Nancy and Peggy. Like you said.'

'Yes?'

I hesitated and then said, 'I prayed for them to come home.'

My Mother stared at me in utter disbelief.

'You did what?'

'For them to come home.'

It seemed my Mother was about to strike me.

'You stupid boy! Come home? And lose their jobs? Are you really so daft? We can't afford to keep them! And there's no jobs here for them!'

'I'm sorry. I just wanted them to come home. What did you want me to pray?'

My Mother sat down in the Best Chair. She'd left her work when she heard me return.

'I don't know,' she said finally, 'I suppose for somebody to be kind to my bairns. But that's too much to ask in this world.'

Twenty Three

WE WERE SITTING, UNCLE FREDDIE AND ME, favoured by a summer sun, upon an old jetty with half the boards missing shore side: stripped to stop anyone using the jetty. We walked tight-rope style out on a bare joist, much as Houdini over Niagara, to reach the remaining planking. It never crossed my mind as I followed Uncle Freddie along the narrow rib that I might fall into the river, or worse upon the bare rocks at low tide. I assumed the gulls circling endlessly were squawking applause at our audacity.

Uncle Freddie and I, legs dangling over the jetty, a dozen open mussels between us, hand line hooks already baited with a mussel tongue tip, awaited the rising of the tide which would bring in with it uncountable shoals of suicidal summer sprats that we would catch in dozens and carry home to eat as our betters gourmandised on whitebait.

'Have you seen this?' Uncle Freddie asked, bringing from his pocket a bedraggled piece of newsprint that had once hung on the nail in our netty until Uncle Freddie had chanced to read and purloin it.

'Corsetry Sale at the Co-op?' I questioned.

Uncle Freddie turned the newsprint over for me.

'RAG MAN BURIES HORSE,' I read, 'Is that Death's... I mean Mr. Butcher?'

My Uncle took the paper from me and read aloud, '*A local dealer has*

168

buried his mare Queenie on Davison's farm. Mr. Davison said, "I have known this horse for years. But don't bring your dogs and cats here. I am not running a pets cemetery."

I said, 'I'm very, very, very glad.'

'Love has many faces,' said Uncle Freddie, 'And Ernie has had a spot of luck. His brother-in-law got drownded.'

'I don't think that was lucky for the brother-in-law,' I commented.

'His sister was married to Weisler,' he continued, 'Weisler's Chandle?'

We pronounced it Whistler, which was a small chandler's catering mostly for trawlers along the lower riverside.

I asked, 'How'd it happen?'

'He got drownded in his cellar.'

'His cellar?'

'It was his party trick. He would raise the trap door, shout *Farewell cruel world!* And jump in.'

'Jump into the cellar?'

'He would jump down on to the ladder. Only this time the cellar was flooded and the ladder wasn't there. So he drownded.'

'And nobody noticed?'

'Not 'til the Saturday when a skipper wanted some pickles.'

I made a secret vow never ever to have a party trick.

'So Ernie and his sister are running the chandle. Well, when they get the cellar pumped and the insurance paid up. They have a mountain of tins with no labels. Every tin's a mystery tour.'

But I was thinking of Mr. Butcher who survived the horror of Gallipoli and yet had humanity enough to lay his faithful companion to rest beneath the turf and not sell her for dog food.

'So, like the school'll be proud of you and your Scholarship, eh?' Uncle Freddie enquired, 'You being like the blue-eyed boy?'

I said, 'I don't have blue eyes.'

'Figure of speech,' Uncle Freddie admitted, 'Racial superiority. You don't get patted on the head by Herr Hitler unless you have blue eyes.'

'I don't want to be patted on the head by Herr Hitler,' I protested.

'So what's up with you and Mrs. Drummond?' my Uncle persisted.

'I wish I hadn't mentioned it now.'

Below us with the rising tide the first stray forerunners of the sprat shoals appeared.

'I thought you liked Mrs. Drummond?' Uncle Freddie persisted, 'I saw what she'd written about you at Christmas. Top marks and that.'

I watched the first flickering shapes passing below and admitted, 'She never was as nice a teacher as Mrs. Armstrong, but now Mrs. Drummond picks on me all the time.'

Uncle Freddie said, 'Yi've always been one of the top lads. So what brought this on then?'

'Billy Drummond didn't get a Scholarship.'

'Her lad?' said my Uncle.

'What am I going to do, Uncle Freddie?'

Uncle Freddie hesitated, 'There's not long to go. Keep your head down, grit your teeth and wait for relief.'

'Billy Drummond's started on me at playtime and on the way home.'

Uncle Freddie looked at me.

'Then stick up for yourself.'

I explained, 'I would, but I can't when he gets two of his pals to hold me so he can bash iss up.'

The flickering shapes in the rising water were multiplying.

My Uncle asked, 'Have you told your Mam?'

'Y'not allowed to squeal.'

Uncle Freddie snorted and said, 'That makes life easy for Billy.'

I regarded the sprats milling about below us like a market crowd hunting bargains.

'I wish I'd never won the Scholarship.'

'What's your Headmaster's name?' my Uncle enquired.

I explained, 'Nobody's allowed to speak to him. There's a law against it.'

Uncle Freddie laughed and said, 'No, there isn't!'

I assured him, 'It says Knock and Wait on his door. You can wait forever. He never comes out.'

Uncle Freddie laughed again and dropped his baited hook down into the swarming sprats.

'Are we here to catch these sprats or not?' he asked and drew up the first silver dancing darling.

It was early morning in our kitchen with me on the fender toasting slices of bread. The kettle was humming on the hob and my Mother was scraping margarine onto my earlier attempts at toast.

'Your Dad's late the morn,' my Mother said, with the slightest trace of anxiety, ' I just hope nothing's up.'

I echoed her anxiety, saying, 'What could be up?'

'You're supposed to be toasting that bread not cremating it,' she responded.

I suggested, 'The black bits make your hair curl.'

'I know who makes my hair curl,' she replied, 'Go and see if Bella's ready for a cup of tea.'

I jumped up, saying, 'Yes, Our Mam!'

My Mother shouted after me, 'Don't take the toast with you, daftie!'

I ran down our stairs and out into the yard. It was one of those wonderful Jarrow mornings with a Dolly-wash blue sky and just a froth of a breeze. A perfect wash and dry day. Not a rag of cloud in the sky. Not even a hint of catastrophe coming.

'Auntie Bella! Are you ready for a cup of tea, Our Mam says?'

'When am I not?' my dear Aunt responded and followed me back into the bottom passage. But I didn't go upstairs. Auntie Bella proceeded alone.

Auntie Bella arrived in our kitchen complaining, 'Oh, that copper fire can be a demon!'

Her sister offered her a mug of hot tea, saying, 'Get yourself round this, Bella.'

'Thanks, Mary,' said my redoubtable Auntie, 'Is Davie away to his bed?'

My Mother said, with growing anxiety, 'His Lordship hasn't put in an appearance yet.'

'He's always so regular,' said Auntie Bella thoughtfully.

It was that moment, heart pounding, lungs bursting, that I tumbled into the kitchen.

'Goodness me, what a commotion!' my Mother cried.

I shouted, 'We've got a letter, Our Mam!'

A letter was a rare event in our house. Any postal delivery boded no good.

'Half of Jarrow must've heard you!' Auntie Bella complained.

'We've had letters before,' said my Mother grudgingly.

I explained, excitedly, 'This is a letter from la belle France, Our Mam!'

'Give it here!' she ordered.

To her surprise I pressed the envelope to my gansey.

'No, it's addressed to me!'

Auntie Bella, in surprise, cried, 'A letter for you, Lecky?'

'Well, at least,' my Mother agreed, 'It's not another catalogue.'

'Go on!' my peerless Aunt encouraged me, 'Open it!'

I tore open the envelope and read the letter as my eyes opened to the size of grapefruit.

'Crumbs!' I cried.

My exasperated Mother cried, 'Well?'

I could hardly frame the words for excitement.

I said, 'It's from the Duke of Windsor. Our late lamented King.'

'I know who he is,' my Mother declared, 'More of Freddie's nonsense!'

'Well,' asked Auntie Bella, 'are you going to tell us what it says?'

I began to read from the letter, which quivered in my hand as I read the wonderful news.

Dear Lecky, Hoping this finds you, as it leaves me, in the pink. Darling Wallis and yours truly have set a date for the nuptials apropos enclosed invite. Wallis is eternally grateful for all you have done for us'

'What did you do for them?' asked my bewildered Aunt.

My Mother interrupted to say, 'Don't start believing this nonsense, Bella, please. I don't want to be the only one visiting the lunatic asylum.'

I continued to read the letter.

'Listen to this!' I cried, and began to read aloud, *'The reception, which will be very swanky, will not be the same if you are not there. Do you fancy being a page boy?'*

Auntie Bella drew a deep breath and cried, 'A page boy?'

She turned to her sister with excitement growing in her eyes, but my Mother said flatly, 'It'll be another of these things he's always writing away for.'

I continued reading from my letter; *'Perhaps your revered mater could run you up a fauntleroy suit in chartreuse?'*

My sweet Aunt again breathed deeply, and exclaimed, 'Oh my, but he'd look sweet in chartreuse!'

My Mother treated her susceptible sister to a frosty glare and remarked, 'Bella, your feet are coming off the ground again!'

'Oh, but he would look positively angelic!' Auntie Bella countered.

My Mother took her sister by both hands, and said, firmly, 'Bella, look at me!' and having assured herself that she did have her sister's attention, she announced, slowly, distinctly, 'He writes these letters to himself, Bella.'

I responded indignantly.

'No, I don't!'

'You should see all these letters from Shirley Temple,' my Mother countered.

'You're not supposed to go into my secret cupboard!' I accused her.

'How'm I to get my black lead brushes then?' she demanded, 'if I cannot get into the fireside cupboard?'

But the battle was not yet lost. Auntie Bella said, 'Go on, Lecky. Read some more!'

My Mother snorted her disapproval, but I finished the letter reading aloud.

'See you ten ack emma, third of June, at the Chateau of Conde in la belle France. There'll be four different jellies and a conjurer. Signing off, forever your pal, David. Formerly King Edward the Eighth.'

With my heart singing, I cried, 'Oh, Our Mam, can I go, please?'

My Mother regarded me as if I had asked her for a King cobra for a pet and cried, 'Of course, you can't go! Don't be so daft!'

Auntie Bella said, wistfully, 'He'd make a darling page boy. With bows at the knee! I can just see him now!'

Encouraged, I persisted, 'Please can I go?'

My Mother turned on her sister.

'Are you mad, encouraging him? It's not real, Bella!'

Defiantly, my beloved Aunt replied, 'The invitation looks real enough to me.'

My Mother hesitated, and said, 'Let me see it.'

She studied the gilt-encrusted cardboard while Auntie Bella and I exchanged smiles of hope and encouragement.

Completing her examination of the royal invitation my Mother said,

'Even if it is real, and I know it's not, we can't afford the fare.'

I countered this objection by reading the final words of my letter.

Triumphantly I declared, '*p.s. Hoping not to give offence to your revered mater, but please find enclosed five pounds to cover expenses.*'

There was a long silence in our kitchen as I drew the five pound note from the envelope.

'Oh, my!' cried Auntie Bella and gave a gasp of wonderment.

'Let me see the money,' ordered my Mother.

She examined the white five pound note, as large as a gentleman's handkerchief.

Auntie Bella exclaimed, reverently, 'The Bank of England Promises to Pay!'

'It's only black writing on white paper,' my Mother commented, 'It must be stage money.'

Suddenly and brutally our discussion on fiscal worth was interrupted by a great roar of rage fit to chill the blood from our bottom passage. Out of the murderous incoherence one word was clear. The monster was shouting my name. For some reason my Father had exploded with anger. There was a thunderous barrage of boots on the stairs.

'Oh, godwit, what's up with Davie?' Auntie Bella cried.

Our Mam enquired, 'What've you done this time, Lecky?'

'Nothing,' I cried, 'I've done nothing!'

Preceded by a peal of thunder my Father burst into the kitchen.

'Where is the little bugger?' he shouted.

My Mother said, 'Now, Davie, calm yourself!'

His eye fell upon me and he advanced with intent to murder.

'Our Mam!' I cried, 'Don't let him at me!'

Auntie Bella pulled me by the arm.

'You get behind me, pet! We'll see if he lays a hand on yi!'

My Father warned her, but stayed his hand.

'This is nowt to do with you, Bella!'

My Mother said, 'You've been drinking!'

She was horrified. Such behaviour was unheard of. My Father ignored her and continued to try to get at me around my redoubtable Aunt.

'The sneaky little bugger. After all I warned him!'

My Mother tried again to placate the angry man.

'Get a grip on yourself, Davie,' she commanded, 'You're frightening the bairn.'

My Father almost exploded with anger.

'Frighten him? I'll do more than that!'

Auntie Bella said, bravely, 'No, you won't!'

My Father ignored the women and threatened me, shouting, 'I warned yi, didn't I? Didn't I? I said it had to stop.'

I tried to divert his anger, offering the Royal Wedding invitation.

'Look, Our Dad, look what's just come!' I said, 'I've been invited to the Duke of Windsor's wedding. And there's a letter.'

My Father stopped raging and said, 'Is that so? Let me see that.'

I gave him both the invitation and the letter. He began to read.

I encouraged him, saying, 'Mrs. Simpson wants me for a page boy.'

'In chartreuse,' Auntie Bella added, 'With bows at the knee.

My Father tore the invitation and the letter into little pieces and dropped them on the floor. I couldn't believe what he'd done. I just stared at him and saw a stranger.

The silence was broken by my Mother who said, 'Oh, Davie, there was no need for that!'

My tongue came unglued and I said, disbelieving, 'He's torn them up, Our Mam!'

'That was a spiteful thing to do, Davie,' said Auntie Bella.

'I'll learn you one way or tother,' was my Father's answer.

My Mother, shocked, said, 'That was unnecessary, surely?'

'I'll tell yi what's unnecessary,' my Father cried, 'This! Another bloody catalogue from Littlewoods. Stuck on the doorstep!'

He flourished the catalogue in our faces, but my Mother was unmoved. She said, 'It's only a catalogue.'

'Where d'y'think the money's coming from to buy rubbish out of catalogues?' he shouted, his anger aflame again.

'It doesn't cost anything to get them,' I said.

My Father looked at me with a fury that was frightening and shouted, 'Yi stupid bairn, we can scarcely keep a roof over our heads. Never mind running oursels into debt with catalogues.'

'We never buy anything,' I countered, 'Our Mam and me just like looking at them. They've got everything in them. I'll show you.'

I offered to take the catalogue from him, but he pulled away.

My Mother said, 'It's harmless fun, Davie.'

'I told yi it had to stop,' he reminded her, 'All this writing away for this and that. Why can't my son be like other bairns?'

'Because he isn't,' my Mother said.

'What's wrong with him?'

Auntie Bella said, 'There's nothing wrong with him.'

I appealed to my Father, asking, 'Can I pick up my invitation, please?'

'Leave it where it is,' he said.

'P'rhaps I could stick it together?' I suggested, but he ignored me.

My Mother said, placatingly, 'Sit down, Davie, and have a cup of tea. This isn't doing any of us any good.'

But my Father was far beyond the bounds of reason; the fences of commonsense had been torn down.

He said, 'I'll have me tea when wi've had a good clear-out of his rubbish.'

He went straight for and opened the fireside cupboard door.

My Mother protested, 'Please leave his cupboard alone.'

I pleaded, 'Stop him Our Mam,' but she was helpless.

He pulled out all my papers, my letters, my stories, my poems and held them to ridicule.

'Just look at this rubbish, Mary. It's like a rat's nest in here.'

Auntie Bella tried to make him see sense.

'Davie, it's the bairn's things. Not yours.'

He countered with, 'Well, I don't know any other bairn like this. Always glawping in corners. Crying at the least bit thing. Look at him now!'

I shouted defiantly, 'I'm not! You couldn't make me cry in a hundred years!'

My Mother tried again, saying, 'They can't all be the same.'

'Well, he's gona grow up,' my Father determined, 'Starting now!'

I cried, 'Not the fire, Our Dad!' but he thrust my papers into the kitchen grate and the flames welcomed the gift. We watched in despair as he filled the grate with my writings and the flames licked up the chimney.

'There y'are. A nice cheerful blaze,' he said, pretending to warm his hands at the flames.

'I'm ashamed of you, Davie,' said Auntie Bella, 'I never thought you could behave like this.'

My Father announced, 'Let that be the end of catalogues in this house.'

My Mother said, 'I hope you're pleased with yourself,' and sat down on a kitchen chair defeated.

My Father, retreating from the scene of his victory announced, 'Don't wake me tonight. I'll get up when I'm good and ready.'

'Aren't you going in?' my Mother asked.

'They're not expecting me,' he said.

'Why ever not?'

'I've had the sack,' he said and left the kitchen, closing the door behind him.

'What does he mean? The sack?' I asked fearfully, but I was ignored.

'Oh, Mary, whatever will you do?' asked Auntie Bella.

She didn't respond.

I asked, fearfully, 'Is it all my fault?'

'Y'just happened to be handy,' my Mother said.

'But what're we going to do?' I pleaded.

She said, 'You're going to school, and we've got work to do.'

My Aunt said, 'I'd best get down to the wash house,' and went quietly from the kitchen. We listened to the whisper of her feet on the stairs.

I had a sudden inspiration and said to my Mother, 'I know what! I'll get a job.'

'What could you do?' she said, 'Apart from make a nuisance of yourself.'

'I could be a Useful Boy.'

She answered, 'There aren't any.'

'They advertise for them in the paper,' I countered, 'Useful Boy wanted.'

'Then be useful. Get yourself ready for school. And don't start him off again.'

Twenty Four

WHEN I GOT BACK FROM SCHOOL I went to see Auntie Bella. She was ironing steadily and her kitchen was as ever an islet of calm amid the raging storm. It had not been my best day at school and I wrote as she ironed, *The weary weight of the brain needs no support from the arm* one hundred times.

As I rested the weary weight of my fingers after ten repetitions of the same tedium I asked my dearest Aunt, 'What's been going on?'

Auntie Bella paused as she changed flat irons and explained, 'Being made nightshift chargehand went to Archie Bragg's head. He thinks he's Mussolini. The manager has no idea what's been going on.'

'But what's that got to do with Our Dad?'

Her iron moving as gracefully as a gliding swan, she said, 'Archie Bragg's been running Davie ragged for weeks now. Niggling at every little thing. Calling him Limpy Dick, would you believe?'

'Why would Our Dad put up with that?'

The dear woman stopped ironing and looked at me.

'Well, to keep you fed, for a start, pet. But last night was the finisher.'

My pen scribed *arm* and stopped.

'What happened?'

'Davie had just loaded one oven, when he stepped back, bumping into the rolley for the next oven, spilling tins and fouling the dough.'

'He'd have the sweat in his eyes,' I remarked, 'I've seen him. It's very hot in the bakery.'

'And Archie Bragg said, "That'll come out of your money, Hopalong." And Davie said, "I'll have another twopennorth," and punched him in the snout.

'Bravo!' I cried and splattered ink across my lines of punishment.

'The punch knocked Archie Bragg off the landing into a flour vat. He was as white as a sheet when they fished him out.'

'Good for Our Dad!' I cried.

'They haven't located Archie's upper denture yet, by the way,' my beloved Aunt said, 'So somebody's going to find a cheery smile in their wholemeal.'

The good lady resumed her ironing and I regarded my ink-splattered page.

'So did Our Dad do a bad thing or a good thing?'

She paused for a moment to say, 'How d'y'mean, pet?'

I explained, 'He's lost his job and that's a bad thing. But he stood up to the bully and that must be a good thing.'

Auntie Bella considered this philosophical whimsy.

'I'm not sure your Mam would agree.'

I commented, 'Nothing is ever straightforward, is it, Auntie Bella?'

I had completed thirty-eight of the lines set as punishment. They were now decorated by a speckling of ink across the page. The problem was whether to start all over again or to think of a really good lie such as that our cat ran across the table when our dog went after it. I decided to stick with the lie.

I was sitting peacefully reading by the bins in the schoolyard when Billy Drummond and his gang found me. Lost in the book I looked up to find Billy sneering down at me. I scrambled to my feet.

Billy said, 'Yi cannot hide from me, Fergie.'

I explained, 'I'm not hiding. I'm reading.'

'What're y'reading?' he demanded.

'*The Prisoner of Zenda*. It wouldn't interest you, Drummer.'

'Let me see it,' he ordered and when I hesitated, 'Hand it over or else I'll bash yi.'

I offered it to him, 'Promise not to tear it? Only it was a present from Auntie Bella. It's a brilliant story.'

Billy tore the cover off the book and offered me the two pieces. His gang laughed to see the dismay on my face.

'Wharrer y'gona tell your auntie now?' he sneered.

In reply I kicked him in the stomach and when he doubled up, I punched him in the face. His gang shouted 'Cheat, cheat, cheat!' and 'Kickyhorse!' as if there were some bullying code that I had broken but Billy Drummond never bothered me again. His mother was not so easily dissuaded.

I stood outside the Headmaster's study until I thought my legs would fall off. When I was finally dragged into the inner sanctum by Mr. Tate as if I were trying to escape he was already in full spate as a drowning river after a cloudburst.

When I tried to explain about Mrs. Drummond, he screamed at me, 'She? She! Who is this She, boy? The cat's mother?'

Bewildered, I said, 'I don't know who the cat's mother is.' Was I under threat of punishment because I didn't know the name of the caretaker's cat's mother? His cat was the only cat I knew.

The little man with the large moustache regarded me with utmost loathing and demanded, 'Do you, by any chance, mean your teacher, Mrs. Drummond? Is this whom you call She?'

Light dawned. This was not an inquisition on cats' nomenclature.

I admitted, 'I mean Mrs. Drummond.'

Mr. Tate was triumphant. He swelled like a tweedy bullfrog to demand, 'And you are determined to persist in saying Mrs. Drummond was wrong?'

He was impatient for my answer.

'Well, boy, speak up!'

'Mrs. Drummond was wrong, sir.'

He rattled the Malacca can against his leg.

'It would appear the Scholarship has swollen your head, boy. Eh, boy?

Is that the problem? Too bigheaded to admit you're wrong!'

'No, sir.'

Mr. Tate smiled the most unholy smile I had ever seen. It was malice accomplished.

'Ah, now we come to the truth! You admit to conceit? Then there is hope for you yet!'

Unfortunately recruitment to the Inquisition ended some hundreds of years ago, but it was evidently Mr. Tate's spiritual home.

'No, sir. I meant no, sir, I don't think I've a swollen head. It's true, sir. Mrs. Drummond told us the wrong way round. The Acropolis is the hill and the ancient city. It's the Parthenon that's the Temple.'

In the silence Mr. Tate exchanged glances with Mrs. Drummond.

The Headmaster said, 'It is cowardly to accuse a lady in these circumstances. Will you play the white man, admit your mistake and apologise to Mrs. Drummond?'

I hesitated and then said, 'How can I, sir? Mrs. Drummond was wrong.'

Mr. Tate said, 'You leave me no alternative. Hold out your hand, boy.'

For one wild and wonderful moment I thought he was about to apologise to me personally. To play the purple-faced white man and shake me by the hand, begging my forgiveness.

'Not to me, boy,' he ordered, 'There. Hold it steady.'

The Malacca cane cut sharply into my palm. The shock of the pain was unbelievable. I found it difficult to hold up my arm.

'Up, up! Hold it up, boy!'

I lifted my faltering arm. I could hear Mr. Tate's breathing quicken. There was an ugly excitement to his respiration. The Malacca again punished my hand with fire and I struggled to cope with the pain.

Through the agony I exclaimed, 'Pheidias set up a beautiful statue on the hilltop, sir.'

The third stroke of the Malacca struck my swollen hand and I cried out, 'A statue of Athena. To whom the Parthenon is dedicated.'

I heard the ugly man's voice shouting, 'Down. Down, I said, boy! Now the left one. Up. Up!'

I raised my left arm, innocent of harm and awaited the agony of the Malacca. The Headmaster was snorting like a pig. I heard the cane coming before it struck and my palm was aflame.

'Sailors could see the shining crest of her helmet. And the top of her spear.'

The fifth stroke was misplaced and struck my fingers. I almost cried out, but the words were my salvation.

'As soon as they rounded the point of Sunium.'

I clenched my teeth as the final stroke struck my burning hand.

'Then they knew they were safely home and their ordeal was ended.'

My heart was beating like a drum. All I could hear was Mr.. Tate's guttural breathing. When I looked at Mrs. Drummond she would not meet my eye.

Mr. Tate, struggling for breath pronounced, 'There, boy. Perhaps that'll teach you?'

I said, 'Thank you very much, sir. Dr. Brewer says there's no education quite like adversity.'

'Furthermore,' declared the monstrous toad, 'I shall write to Mr. Turnstone at the Grammar School and expose your lack of moral fibre.'

He smiled at me. His triumph was complete.

There came a knocking at the study door.

'Wait!' called Mr. Tate imperiously.

The office door opened and the Headmaster cried, 'Are you deaf? I said, wait!'

My Uncle Freddie stood in the doorway. I was simultaneously drowned in relief and apprehension.

My Uncle Freddie said, politely, 'I'm sorry, Mr. Tate, but' and on seeing me, 'What's going on here?'

The Headmaster waved the Malacca at my Uncle and ordered him, 'Kindly leave my study this instant, sir!'

'What's going on, Lecky?' Uncle Freddie said, ignoring both the Malacca and the little fat man waving the cane at him.

'Mrs. Drummond sent me to the Headmaster for contradicting her, but she was wrong,' I answered him.

Mr. Tate, purple of face, asserted himself once again, crying, 'Will you leave my study, sir?'

'When I'm ready,' my Uncle replied, and to me, 'You're sure Mrs.

Drummond was wrong?'

I looked at Mrs. Drummond who did not meet my eye. She was pale and shaken.

Indignantly, Mr. Tate responded, 'What would you know about the matter, sir?'

Uncle Freddie said, 'I know my nephew.'

'Your nephew? This boy is your nephew?' demanded the Headmaster.

Uncle Freddie ignored Mr. Tate and asked me again, 'You are absolutely sure? Honour bright?'

I nodded my head. My hands were puffy and swollen. The pain was pulsing up my arms.

'Honour bright, Uncle Freddie,' I said, 'But Mr. Tate wouldn't believe me.'

Mrs. Drummond said, 'Perhaps I,' and was interrupted by the Headmaster, who reiterated, 'The boy has taken against his teacher and persists in making trouble for her.'

Mrs. Drummond gave an unhappy cry and fled from the study.

My Uncle said, 'I think you have that the wrong way round, Mr. Tate,' and to me, 'Go on, old son!'

'Then Mr. Tate gave me six of the worst.'

I held out my tormented hands in pale imitation of the painting above Mr. Tate's desk showing Christ displaying his wounds to his Disciples.

Without any warning my Uncle Freddie seized hold of the Headmaster by the scruff of his neck, dislodging his celluloid collar.

A shocked Mr. Tate cried out, 'What do you think you're doing?'

Similarly shocked, I cried, 'Uncle Freddie!' in disbelief.

Mr. Tate struggled helplessly in my Uncle's iron grip as he disarmed him of the Malacca and thrust the little fat man across his desk. Inkpot, blotting paper pad, books, vase, photograph frame, all came crashing to the floor.

The Headmaster cried in muffled tones, 'How dare you, sir! Unhand me! Unhand me this instant, sir!'

Uncle Freddie ignored his bleatings and asked, 'How many whacks did he give you?'

The little fat man wriggled helplessly and cried, 'Don't you dare, sir!'

I answered, 'Six. But, Uncle Freddie!'

As my Uncle raised the Malacca, Mr. Tate squeaked, 'Let go of me! I warn you! I shall have the police on you!'

Mr. Tate's final words dissolved into a scream of pain as my Uncle Freddie proceeded to lay six weighted strokes across the pedagogue's plump buttocks. The Headmaster screamed throughout the punishment. When Uncle Freddie finished dispensing justice he broke the Malacca into two pieces. Mr. Tate lay weeping on his desk. Uncle Freddie and I left the study and closed the door.

Twenty Five

DOWN BY THE RIVER THE TIDE lay at ease. It was that moment when all energy exhausted, the water is still as a millpond 'til the turning tide begins again at the command of the unseen moon.

I was on my knees with my hands deep in salt water. Uncle Freddie sat beside me. We looked across at the farther shore and listened to voices and sounds as from another room, another world.

When I took a hand from the water to scratch my nose, Uncle Freddie said, 'Keep your hands in the water. The brine'll do them good.'

I looked at his sombre features and he said, 'What?'

'I wish you hadn't done that.'

He laughed and assured me, 'I haven't enjoyed anything so much for ages.'

'You'll have to go on the run,' I assured him.

'Keep your hands in the water,' he said.

'When they catch up with you, you'll have to wear a suit covered in arrows and be locked in a damp, cold cell and eat bread and water.'

Uncle Freddie said, 'Mr. Tate won't call the pollis.'

'Why won't he?'

My Uncle explained, 'His vanity won't allow him. He'd be the laughing stock of Jarrow. But he might have a few sharp words with Mrs. Drummond.'

I felt a great weight lift from my shoulders.

'D'y'think so?'

Uncle Freddie said, 'Let's see those hands.'

'They creak when I bend the fingers.'

Uncle Freddie examined my hands.

'Fat as muffins and red as beetroot. Soak them a while longer.'

I said, 'I thought Mr. Tate was better than Mrs. Drummond. But he wasn't, was he?'

'Did I ever tell you about Jackie Tatters?'

I shook my head.

'I don't think so.'

'When Jackie was dying in Ormonde Street gutter with folk stepping over him, thinking he was drunk, Ali Jamjar picked him up.'

'Was he often drunk?'

'Jackie was always drunk,' said my Uncle.

Two gulls alighted near us, heads turning, gold eyes watching to listen to the story.

'Ali cleaned the vomit from his face and saw Jackie was dying.'

I interrupted to ask, 'How did he know that?'

My Uncle said, 'Ali's seen a lot of men die. So he took Jackie on his cart to Palmer's Hospital so he could die in a bed.'

'That was very kind of him.'

'Men and women in their Saturday best laughed to see Jackie riding on the cart and foolish bairns ran alongside shouting.'

Curious, I asked, 'Who was Jackie Tatters really?'

'The squarest bloke in Jarrow. Finest footballer I ever saw.'

'What happened to make him Jackie Tatters?'

'The QUEEN MARY blew up at Jutland. Admiral Beatty said, *There seems to be something wrong with our bloody ships today.* Only six men survived the QUEEN MARY. One of them became Jackie Tatters.'

Uncle Freddie was quiet for a moment, and then he said, 'It might've been better, if Jackie Tatters had died in the battle.'

'It would've been better if there was no battle,' I said, 'But I'm proud of Mr. Jamjar. I shall always think of him as the Good Samaritan.'

Uncle Freddie said, 'Well, here's a question for you, professor.'

I hastened to assure him, 'I'm not a professor yet.'

'Did Ali behave like that because he is a ragman or is Ali a ragman because he behaves like that? Conversely, did Mr. Tate beat you because he is a headmaster or is he a headmaster because he likes to beat children?'

'That's a very hard question, Uncle Freddie,' I said.

My Uncle arose and dusted off his trousers.

He said, 'There's something I have to do.'

I felt a similar urgency and announced, 'There's something I have to do too.'

My Uncle said, 'I should've done it sooner. Never put off 'til tomorrow what you should do today.'

'No, Uncle Freddie.'

As he moved to leave he said, 'Steep those hands until the ferry comes back across the water. I'll let your Mam know you haven't run off.'

I did indeed have an important task to undertake; a pilgrimage that takes us into the steam, smoke and clamour of Hawick railway station where a Railway Guard held a firm grip on my collar.

He waited patiently as a porter completed the litany, 'Hawick! All change! Hawick! All change for Waverley!'

'Here, Tommy, keep this young rascal safe for ten minutes, will you?' was his request to the porter.

The porter eyed me with curiosity.

'What's he done, then, Arthur?'

'Travelling without a ticket,'

'Oh, dear, oh, dear, oh, dear! That's a hanging matter that is!' the porter sympathised to me.

Alarmed, I protested, 'It doesn't say so on the posters.'

The Guard surrendered me into the porter's care and the old man led me off to a dusty, echoing Parcels Room where the busy clamour of the station faded away. He sat me on an empty pigeon hamper and said, 'You stay there like a good lad, and mebbes I'll find you a cup of tea. Would you like that now?'

'Yes, please, sir,' I answered, and 'Sir?'

'What's going to happen to me?'

The porter blew out his cheeks and shook his head.

'There's no hangings in Hawick on a Wednesday. Half day closing. You'll have to bide the morn when the hangman comes.'

I promised him, 'Our Mam would be very upset if you hang me.'

'Don't fash yourself, sonny,' he reassured me, 'I expect they'll tell your Mammy and she'll rescue you from the gallows in the nick of time.'

'And if she doesn't?'

His head jerked to one side, his tongue popped out of his mouth, and he gave a first-rate impression of a man dancing and kicking on the end of a rope. It was very reassuring.

As soon as he ambled off chuckling to himself, I too quit the Parcels Room and walked out of the station. All I had to do now was traverse the fells to Panhacklety House. I started out boldly enough on the Jedburgh road, but night and rain fell together driving me to a field barn where a light glowed through the chinks.

As I approached the barn with the rain running down my neck into my shirt I realised that there was someone sheltering in the barn. With some effort I prised open the little-used door.

There was a figure sitting at the farther end of the barn by the lamp. I hesitated, but the rain at my back was unrelenting. The noise of the rain had drowned the noise of my approach and entry.

Twenty Six

'EXCUSE ME, SIR,' I CALLED, 'could I come in out of the rain?'

The man by the primus stove stirred and turned towards me. He said, 'Well, now if this don't beat all!'

I recognised him with a lightening of the heart.

'Mister Service!' I cried.

Robert Service, wartime ambulance driver, people's poet, Canuck bum and friend of my Uncle Freddie stood up and bowed to me.

'At your service, Lecky!'

I hastened to join him in the lamplight.

I assured him, 'Oh, Mister Service, am I pleased to see you?'

'Likewise. Somewhat surprised, but delighted to renew your acquaintance, mon vieux.'

I explained, 'It was getting very dark.'

Robert Service looked beyond me and said, 'Is your admirable Uncle not with you?'

'No, he said he had something else he had to do.'

'What're you doing on the road?' the poet enquired.

I said, 'I've just escaped the gallows, Mister Service.'

He accepted this explanation without question and said, 'Then you've timed your entry to perfection, Lecky. My plucky primus is just now delivering the goods. What would you say to a mug of hot Irish-stew-in-the-name-of-the-law?'

Delighted, I answered, 'I would say, thank you very much.'

Indicating a straw bale, Mr. Service invited me, 'Then park your carcass, pardner and tell me your story.'

The old poet had that rare quality of illuminating darkness. Fear, despair, loneliness, all twilight's jackals retreated before him as I told him my recent history.

'That sure is bad luck on your father, mon ami. But it's not the end of the world. It's just been chipped a little. But d'y'think you've done the wise thing, hiking out here? Without informing your maman?'

'Uncle Freddie said, don't put it off 'til tomorrow. I just have to get a job now Our Dad's lost his.'

The poet nodded his understanding.

'Maybe when you reach the House your sister could send a telegram tomorrow?'

'Yes, I expect that's what she'll do.'

I sipped my nourishing stew, which filtered warmth and courage into my innermost being.

'D'y'reckon Lord and Lady Look-down-their-noses'll give you a job at this House?'

'They've given Nancy and Peggy jobs.'

Robert Service wrinkled his nose, puffed on his pipe and suggested, 'I suspect they're both powerful workers.'

I protested, 'I could be a stable boy. Or I could lick their boots. You do that with the aristocracy.'

The old poet smiled and said, 'Here, lick out the billie for practice and I'll tell you a story for dessert.'

Taking the warm can with its lingering traces of the finest meal I had ever eaten, I agreed, 'Yes, please.'

'Do I have your attention?' my Canadian friend enquired.

'At your service, Mister Service!'

Putting aside the billie, I settled down to listen. In the lamplight and the glow of the primus, nestled in a straw armchair with night and rain beating on our roof the old barn was a magic kingdom.

'There was once a Lord of the Swans,' began Robert Service, 'who knew every safe water and swamp, every rich river and lake and his cobs, pens and cygnets prospered over many seasons. But the Lord grew old and careless and finally led his flock into an ambush.'

Caught up in the story, I breathed, 'Oh, no!'

'Oh, yes!' the old poet continued, 'A rain of lead struck down cob, pen and cygnet in blood and feathers. Amongst the screams of terror there were those, forgetful of the good years, who cursed their Lord with dying breath, but a young swan, mortally stricken, twined his neck about his dying leader, and as they fell together, cried out, joyfully, 'See, lord, see, I die too!'

We sat in a silence that magnified the clamour beating on our shelter from the stormy blast. Somewhere out in the night a beast cried fitfully.

I said, 'That's a very strange story.'

The old man said, 'I guess it's about loyalty. Which is either the supreme virtue. Or an unforgivable sin.'

'What d'y'mean, Mister Service?'

'Let's say I don't believe your father would want you to lick Lord and Lady Snootygoose's boots. But that's just the opinion of an old bum Canuck.'

Mr. Service and I stood in the shelter of the laurels and regarded Panhacklety House. It was a large, sprawling gentleman's country residence complete with east and west wing, lead-topped turrets and castellated roof line, a bulldog of a house, scowling at the pleasant pastoral scene.

Mr. Service said, 'This it?'

'Yes,' I said.

I could see a small figure, in a dress too large, a hessian apron and a shapeless cap, scrubbing the front steps of Panhacklety House. It was my sister Peggy.

'Then I shall leave you to negotiate employment,' said the poet. 'But remember, Lecky, mon vieux, *'The rich know not the worth of anything, But the poor rejoice to hear the blackbird sing.'*

I informed him, 'Whenever I hear the blackbird sing now I'll remember you, Mister Service.'

We shook hands in farewell and the poet retreated to climb back over the estate wall; a feat he accomplished nimbly on our ingress despite having lost a foot boarding a freight train in America.

The image of that boot and foot lying on the track as the train steamed towards the horizon singing its mournful song in the midnight dark has haunted me for a lifetime. What wild creature first approached to sniff the bloody leather?

A man walked up the steps and into the House over the shining limestone my sister had washed. Peggy came to wipe away his footmarks and returned to scrubbing.

I walked across a league of lawn towards the sound of the scrubbing brush.

'Hello, Peggy!' I said.

My sister jumped to her feet, almost overturning her bucket.

'Lecky?' she cried, disbelievingly, 'What're you doing here?'

She looked round to see if we were observed and wiped her red hands on her apron.

'I've come for a job.'

Peggy laughed uncertainly and exclaimed, 'Don't be daft! You're going to the Grammar School.'

'Not any more,' I replied, 'Our Dad's lost his job so I have to get one.'

'He hasn't!' she exclaimed, 'Not Our Dad? Tell me it's not true!'

I nodded sadly and said, 'It's true.'

Peggy made her decision.

'We can't stand here. Come on!'

She picked up her bucket and scrubbing brush, seized me by the hand and repeated, 'Come on!'

'Where are we going?'

Peggy said, determinedly, 'We'll have to find Nancy.'

We ran, Peggy and I, across the gravel, keeping low beneath the front windows, the bucket banging against her leg, and round the side of the House. We ran under an archway and into a yard where a gig stood without a horse.

'Nobody'll see us here,' Peggy said and we slowed to a walk, breathing heavily. Across the yard was an open door. We went through the door into an echoing corridor that rattled our disturbed breathing round the walls.

Peggy explained, 'Nancy should be somewheres,' and called in a strident stage whisper, 'Nancy!'

We advanced farther down the corridor into a stairwell where a staircase seemed to rise forever in a spiral.

Peggy called to a figure on the staircase, 'Nancy!'

Nancy was polishing the balustrade, her back bent as a crescent moon. When she straightened up I saw how my mother must've looked as a young girl.

Nancy said, 'What now?'

'Look who's turned up!' Peggy announced.

Only then did my sister recognise me.

'Lecky?' she cried, 'Is something wrong with Our Mam?'

Peggy assured her, 'No. He's come to get a job because' and I interrupted to announce, 'Our Dad's lost his job.'

Nancy dropped her polishing rag.

'Oh, no!' she cried.

'So I thought,' I said.

Nancy came down the stairs in three giant steps to confront me.

'That'll make it easier for Our Mam, will it, you bolting off?' she demanded, 'I presume she didn't give her blessing?'

I stood abashed, and said, humbly, 'I thought you could send a telegram not to worry.'

Nancy looked at me as if I had suggested she eat a dish of sour milk and spiders.

'Well, there's no problem there!' she announced, her tone dripping with sarcasm, 'Kindly replace the receiver, your Ladyship, I wish to send an urgent telegram.'

'They must be worried sick,' Peggy contributed.

I suggested, 'I thought you would help me get a job as a stable boy?'

Nancy laughed bitterly and said, 'I couldn't get you a job as a stable door.'

We stood in silence in the stairwell while Nancy thought what to do.

'Get him upstairs, Peggy, before somebody sees him,' she sighed.

Somewhat downhearted I followed Peggy through a maze of corridors and stairs until, at last, she lifted the latch on a plain pine door and we entered a small attic under the eaves.

Peggy announced proudly, 'This is our room.'

'The roof comes right down on your head,' I commented, but was ignored by my sister.

'We have our own beds and our own washstand and jug and bowl. And our own window.'

I crossed in two steps to peer out of the tiny window.

'You can't see much,' I said.

Peggy continued to list my sisters' blessings.

'Her Ladyship has given us our own Bible so we can read and say our prayers at night. But we have to buy our own candles.'

'Why d'y'have to buy your own candles?'

'Mrs. Reed, she's the housekeeper says, otherwise we'd burn them all night long. Which is only fair.'

Peggy's pride and pleasure in their little domain was rudely interrupted when the latch lifted and the door opened. Peggy shrank back when an older lady with the face of a dried prune entered. It was, unfortunately, Her Ladyship.

In an icy voice, Her Ladyship, demanded, 'What is this boy doing here?'

Poor Peggy was petrified.

'Oh, your Ladyship!' was all she could pronounce, eyes popping from her head.

Her Ladyship, fixed a gimlet glare upon my sister and repeated the question.

'I said, what is this boy doing in my house?'

A witless Peggy returned the compliment by repeating, 'Oh, your Ladyship!'

Her Ladyship stamped her foot on the bare boards and insisted, 'For goodness sake, girl, stop repeating, *your ladyship!*'

Peggy immediately burst into tears and began to wail hysterically. Her Ladyship slapped my sister's face and demanded, 'Stop that dreadful noise and answer my question!'

Peggy subsided into sobs and I said, 'I'm her brother and I've come—'

The harridan turned to look at me as she would at a retriever that had disgraced itself in the drawing room. Every word was coated in ice.

'Did I give you permission to speak?'

I stammered, 'No. I just thought'

She turned from me and demanded of Peggy, 'Speak up, you silly girl!'

Punctuated by sobs, Peggy managed to say, 'He's my brother and he's come here because,' but was interrupted by Nancy entering to announce, 'I've sent a telegram so at least they'll know'

Nancy became painfully aware of Her Ladyship's presence, but her tongue continued, regardless of her brain, to say, 'the little bugger's not drowned himself.'

'Did I hear you correctly, Nancy?' said Her Ladyship icily.

'I didn't mean to say *bugger*, your Ladyship,' apologised Nancy, 'It just popped out.'

Her Ladyship ignored this apology to ask, 'You have used the telephone without my permission?'

Nancy said, stoutly, 'Yes, your Ladyship. To reassure our Mother that—'

'Enough! I wish to hear no excuses.'

Her Ladyship silenced my sister and turned to me.

'Turn out your pockets, boy!'

Nancy, shocked, intervened to say, 'Your Ladyship, please! My brother is not a thief!'

'Turn out your pockets,' Her Ladyship continued, 'or I shall call someone to do it for you.'

'Shall I, Nancy?' I asked.

My sister surrendered, saying, 'Just don't wave your dirty snotrag about.'

I emptied my petty treasures onto the nearest bed. Her Ladyship pounced on one crumpled item.

'What is this? A five pound note!'

Nancy cried, 'Oh, Lecky!'

Three astonished faces stared at me, Peggy's swollen raspberry fool, Nancy wearing Our Mam's face, and the triumphant sneer of the Witch of Panhacklety.

'May one enquire,' Her Ladyship asked, 'where you acquired this bank note?'

I answered truthfully, 'The Duke of Windsor sent it so I could go to his wedding as a pageboy in chartreuse with ribbons at the knee.'

There was a long silence in the attic room. Both Peggy and Nancy would not meet my eye. Her Ladyship folded up my five pound note and placed it in the beaded bag she wore on her wrist.

Her Ladyship said, 'I think you'll be a very lucky boy to escape birching as well as a term of imprisonment.'

We stood outside the lodge gates, one small boy, lacking moral fibre, two bewildered sisters, lacking employment and two very large boxes.

Nancy said, 'Well done, Lecky! There is now no one in this family who has a job.'

I said, 'I'm very, very sorry.'

Peggy punched me in the back and accused me, 'You're sorry? I was feeling sorry for meself scrubbing the front steps, but now I'm sorry I'm not.'

'She kept my five pound note,' I complained.

Nancy explained, 'The upper classes turn a profit on everything.'

I surveyed the ancient countryside, the silent bucolic lane.

'How're we going to get home?' I asked.

'Walk. And it's a long walk over Carter Bar. So we'd best get started.'

Peggy baulked and asked, 'But how're we going to manage our boxes?'

The two chests, proudly painted with my sisters' names by my Father, grew larger with every glance.

'I'll carry one,' I offered.

I struggled to lift Nancy's box and failed.

My sister said, 'You can't even lift it.'

I boasted, 'Just let me work my strength up. I can do it.'

Then in the distance, growing louder with every gust of breeze there came a familiar bugle note and every now and then a familiar cry.

'I know that voice,' said Nancy.

Peggy said, 'It's the ragabone man.'

'It's Ali Jamjar!' I cried, 'In the nick of time! That's two nicks of time I've had!'

Inquisitive Peggy asked, 'What was the other one?'

'I nearly got hung in Hawick.'

Twenty Seven

ROUND THE BEND CAME THE FAMILIAR FIGURE of Bucephalus and Ali Jamjar walking at his head and the cart following on. At the sight of our despondent band, Bucephalus slowed down, turning his head questioningly to Ali Jamjar. The cart stopped and Ali Jamjar surveyed the survivors of the shipwreck, stranded on an alien shore.

'What have we here? A Fergie family outing?' enquired the wearer of the Black Prince's ruby.

'Oh, Mister. Jamjar, I'm so glad to see you!' I cried.

Nancy said, 'We're in terrible trouble!'

'Trouble?' enquired Ali Jamjar, 'What trouble?'

Nancy answered, 'It's too long a story to tell now.'

'Please can we have a ride home to Jarrow, Mister Jamjar?' Peggy begged.

Ali Jamjar looked into her tearstained face and smiled a smile that wiped away her fears.

'With pleasure, my darling,' he said, 'Are those your boxes?'

Nancy warned him, 'They're very heavy,' but Ali swung the boxes up on to the cart with an ease I envied.

'Climb up, ladies,' he called, 'I think it's time we all went home to canny auld Jarrer.'

'Thank you, Mister Jamjar,' said Nancy with heartfelt relief.

But this pleasant sense of relief was disturbed by an angry voice from within the great iron gates of Panhacklety House.

'Hi, you!' cried a red-faced man in corduroy, thwacking his leg with a stout ashplant, 'Shift it!'

Ali Jamjar enquired of Nancy, 'Who's this?'

'It's Mr. Beestie, his Lordship's agent.'

Ali Jamjar called to the apoplectic agent.

'Are you speaking to me?'

Mr. Beestie advanced through the manorial gates to announce, 'His Lordship's car's on its way from the House and he won't want you squatting in the gateway.'

'I'm going,' said Ali Jamjar amiably enough, to which the agent answered aggressively, 'Aye, well, shift the cart, top speed.'

Ali Jamjar lowered the reins and suggested, 'A little politeness wouldn't come amiss.'

Anxiously, Nancy advised Ali Jamjar, 'Don't argue with him, Mr. Jamjar. Let's just go!'

Mr. Beestie cried, 'The lass is right. Shift it, Sambo!'

In the distance a car horn sounded. The agent turned away and began to open the great iron gates.

'What did you call me?' asked Ali Jamjar.

'Oh, no!' I cried because I knew what was going to happen next.

Mr. Beestie paused in his task to reply, 'I said shift it, Sambo!'

I cried out to the agent who seemed oblivious of his danger, 'Yi've done it now, Mister Beestie! Mister Jamjar flattened Karl Kronstadt flatter than the paper on the wall.'

Mr. Beestie, who hadn't opened the gates more than a squeak turned his attention to Ali Jamjar.

'Are yi gona shift it? Or shall I do it for yi?' he demanded.

Ali Jamjar turned to me, saying, 'Hold the reins, Lecky.'

I took the reins and Ali Jamjar climbed down from the cart.

I shouted to the agent, 'Run for your life, Mr. Beestie!'

The red-faced man in corduroy raised a wavering ashplant at Ali Jamjar and threatened, 'You lay a finger on me, Sambo, and His Lordship'll have you locked up faster than you can spit.'

Nancy cried, 'Please, Mr. Jamjar, don't do anything.'

Ali Jamjar didn't spit nor did he lay a finger on Mr. Beestie. He lifted the iron gates off their hinges and dropped them in the gateway. The gates fell with an horrendous crash as his Lordship's limousine arrived and braked, but failed to avoid striking the fallen gates.

In the awestricken silence that followed upon this Herculean feat Ali Jamjar recited, '*So shall we throw down the shackles of slavery that you may bear their weight,*' which seemed to me most appropriate in the circumstances.

My sisters and I clapped the hero who modestly returned to his seat and singing most of the way, we walked Bucephalus over Carter Bar and rode home to canny auld Jarrow

Twenty Eight

SUNLIGHT AND SWEET WILLIAM on the kitchen windowsill. A linen snowfall blotting out our shabby table. There is the clash of the oven door, the clatter of plates and noses lifted in the air inhaling the full savour of Sunday dinner. The Fergusons et alia are about to dine. My grandparents are here; Grandfather subdued and Grandmother as faded as old lace. The girls are here; Nancy and Peggy juggling cutlery and plates. It is an unusual special occasion as the guest of honour is absent.

Auntie Bella said, 'Is that everything, Mary?'
My Mother surveyed the table with satisfaction.
'I think that's it, Bella,' she said.
Nancy begged her, 'Come and sit down, Our Mam. If there's anything I'll get it.'
My Mother sat down at table and sighed with contentment.
'Now, before your father carves, Lecky'll say grace for us,' she decided.
My Father said, 'No, he won't.'
My Mother gave him a hurt look and pleaded, 'Oh, Davie, don't start.'
Peggy said, 'You won't start anything, will you, Our Dad?'
'I just want to say grace in me own house,' the infuriating man said.
Nancy said, 'Go on then, Our Dad.'

Reluctantly we agreed and my Mother urged, 'Mind what you say, Davie!'

My Father looked around our apprehensive company and recited, '*Thank God for the taties and beans.*'

'Davie!' my Mother warned, but he was not to be deterred.

'*The same for the fresh bread and cheese, So hurry up and send it, Though we know where it'll end up, For we're all getting pains in our knees.*'

'Amen!' I cried and the whole company laughed.

My Mother lifted her glass of stout and proposed the toast, 'Absent friends!'

We all raised our glasses in respect, chiming 'Absent friends!' Silence fell and we began our meal.

My father said, 'God bless Freddie!'

We all looked towards Auntie Bella who smiled, and said, 'The silly man! I could just shake him!'

My beloved Uncle was missing from our company because he was in Durham Gaol spending three months picking oakum for caning Mr. Tate. But before he was arrested he got my Father's job back for him by spilling the beans on Archie Bragg; which he would never have done for himself.

I had brought our Nancy and Peggy home again for a spell and it was Ernie Butcher who gave them jobs running a stall in the market selling off his tins with no label. But it was Nancy who turned selling unlabelled tins at a penny each into a flourishing business selling four for thruppence and a penny back if you didn't get at least one tin of meat. It was such a success Mr. Butcher was buying in any bankrupt stock of dog food and removing the labels.

But I never got the octopus.

I remember most clearly the faces round that table and the love that held us together through adversity and illuminated our sunlit days. I remember my brave Uncle Freddie who thought that justice should be done whatever the cost and my Auntie Bella who offered no complaint and sought no comfort.

After all these years the circle isn't broken though the hands I hold most tightly I cannot see, but we are still all holding hands, Our Mam and Dad and Bella and Freddie and Nancy and Peggy, Granny and Grandad and me.

Take hold of all you love, take hold and never let them go. Take tight hold and never ever let them go.